101 SONGS FOR EASY GUITAR

Wise Publications
London/New York /Sydney

THIS PUBLICATION IS NOT AUTHORISED
FOR SALE IN THE UNITED STATES
OF AMERICA AND/OR CANADA.

Exclusive distributors:
Music Sales Limited,
8/9 Frith Street, London W1V 5TZ, England
Music Sales Pty. Limited
120, Rothschild Avenue, Rosebery, NSW 2018, Australia

This book © Copyright by Wise Publications
ISBN 0.86001-511.4
AM 21171

Printed in Great Britain by Redwood Books, Trowbridge, Wiltshire

Rock Me On The Water

Words and music by Jackson Browne

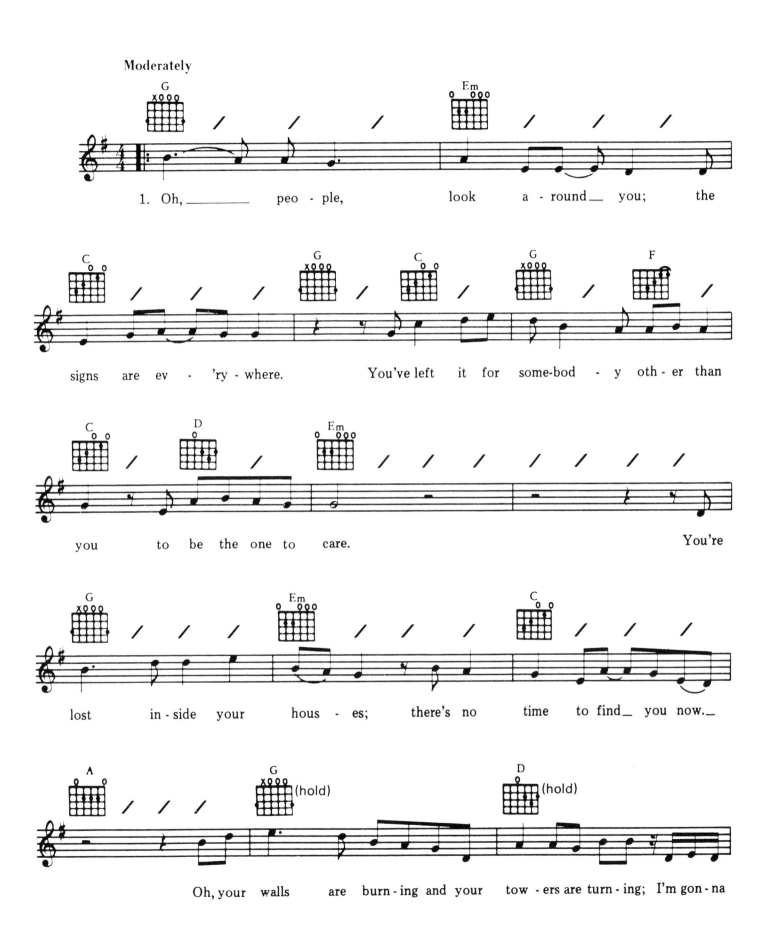

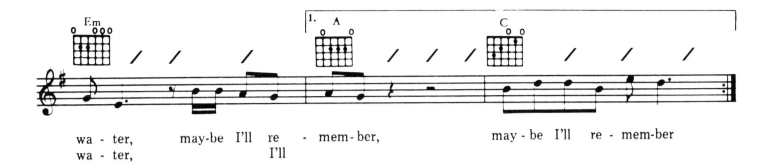

wa - ter, may-be I'll re - mem - ber, may - be I'll re - mem-ber
wa - ter, I'll

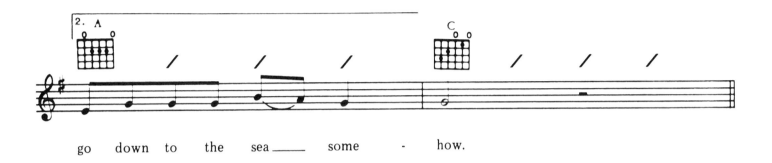

go down to the sea _____ some - how.

Repeat and fade

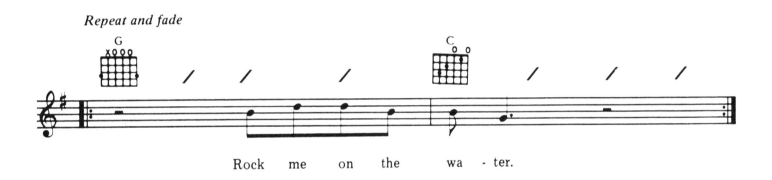

Rock me on the wa - ter.

2. The road is filled with homeless souls, every woman, child and man
   Who have no idea where they will go, but they'll help you if they can.
   But everyone must have some thought that's gonna pull them through somehow.
   Oh, the fires are raging hotter and hotter, but the sisters of the sun are gonna
   rock me on the water now.

3. Oh, people, look among you, it's there your hope must lie.
   There's a seabird above you gliding in one place like Jesus in the sky.
   We all must do the best we can and then hang on to that Gospel plow.
   When my life is over I'm gonna stand before the Father, but the sisters of the sun are gonna
   rock me on the water now.

Revolution

Words and music by John Lennon and Paul McCartney

Moderate Steady Beat

Starting note for singing:

You say you want a rev-o-lu-tion, Well,_ you know,_

We all want to change the world.___ You tell me that it's e-vo-

lu-tion. Well,_ you know,_ We all want to change the world.___

But when you talk a-bout de-struc-tion,___

Don't you know that you can count me out, Don't you know it's gon-na

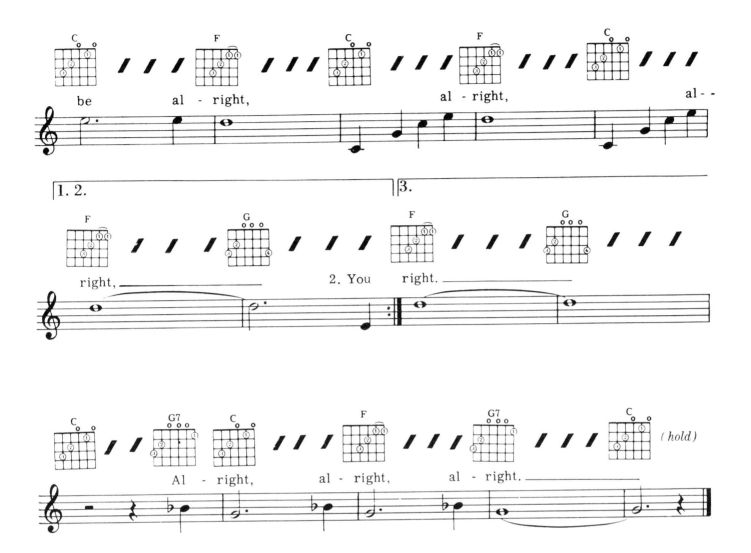

be al - right, al - right, al --

1. 2.

right, 2. You right.

3.

Al - right, al - right, al - right. *(hold)*

You say you got a real solution,
Well, you know, we'd all love to see the plan.
You ask me for a contribution.
Well, you know, We are doing what we can.
But when you want money for people with minds that hate,
All I can tell you is brother you have to wait
Don't you know it's gonna be alright, alright, alright,

You say you'll change the constitution,
Well, you know, We all want to change your head.
You tell me it's the institution.
Well, you know, You better free your mind instead.
But if you go carrying pictures of Chairman Mao,
You ain't going to make it with anyone anyhow,
Don't you know it's gonna be alright, alright, alright.

Without Her

Words and music by Harry Nilsson

Moderately

I spend the night in a chair___ think-in' she'll be there,___ but she
It's just no good an-y-more___ when you walk through the door___ of an

nev-er comes,___ And then I wake up and wipe the sleep from my eyes,___ And I
emp-ty room,___ And then you go in-side___ and set a ta-ble for one,___ It's so

rise to face an-oth-er day WITH-OUT HER. Mm ___
fun to spend an-oth-er day WITH-OUT HER.

Mm ___ Mm ___

We burst the pret-ty bal-loon,___ it took us to the moon___ such a

beau-ti-ful thing. ___ But it's end-ed now and it sounds like a lie,___ if I

Repeat and Fade

Down By The River

Words and music by Neil Young

Purple Haze
Words and music by Jimi Hendrix

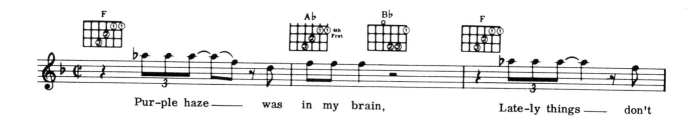

Pur-ple haze ——— was in my brain,   Late-ly things ——— don't

seem the same,   Act- in' fun-ny,   but I   don't know why,

'Scuse me ——————— while I   kiss the sky.

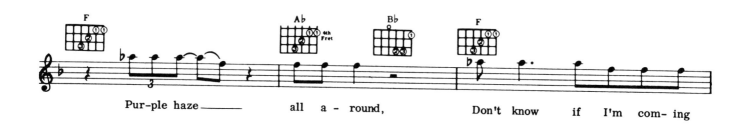

Pur-ple haze——— all a - round,   Don't know   if   I'm com- ing

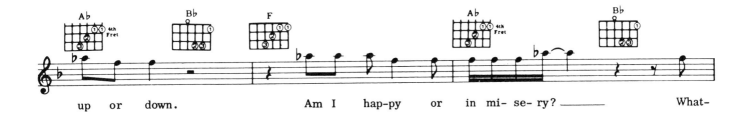

up or down.　　　　　Am I hap-py or in mi- se- ry? _____ What-

e - ver it is,____ that girl　　put a　　spell on me!

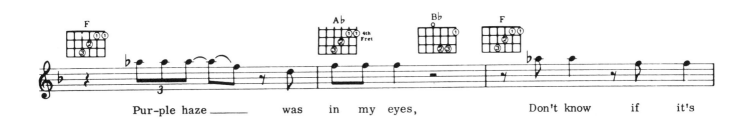

Pur-ple haze ____　　was in my eyes,　　　Don't know if it's

day or night.　　　You've got me blow-ing,　　blowin' my mind. Is it

to - mor - row　　or just the　　end of time?

Take It Easy

Words and music by Jackson Browne and Glen Frey

Moderate Country style

1. Well, I'm a - run-nin' down the road try'n' to loos-en my load, I've got

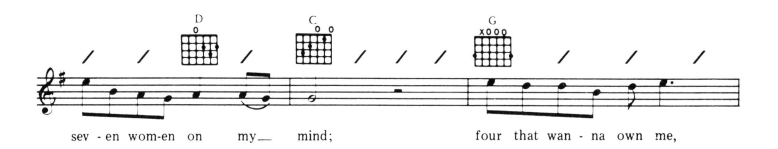

sev-en wom-en on my__ mind; four that wan-na own me,

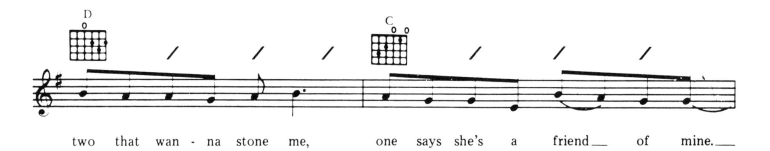

two that wan-na stone me, one says she's a friend__ of mine.__

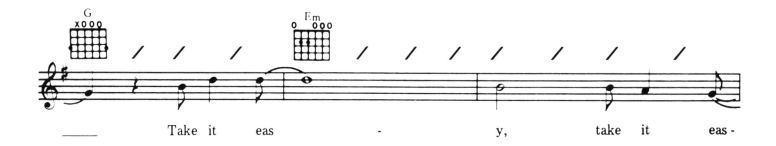

____ Take it eas - y, take it eas-

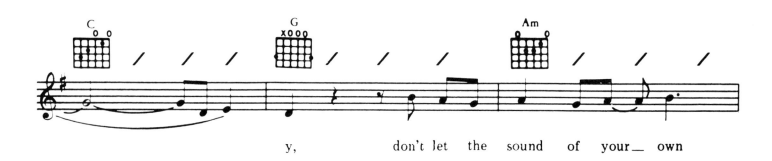

y, don't let the sound of your__ own

wheels _ drive you cra - zy. Light - en up _

_ while you still can, _ don't e - ven try to un - der - stand, _

_ just find a place to make _ your stand and take it eas -

To Coda ⊕ 1.   2. *D. S.* 𝄉 *(lyric 3) al Coda* ⊕

y. _   2. Well, I'm a -   y. _   3. Well, I'm a -

Coda
⊕

me. _____

2. Well, I'm a-standin' on a corner in Winslow, Arizona, and such a fine sight to see,
It's a girl, my Lord, in a flat-bed Ford slowin' down to take a look at me.
Come on, baby, don't say maybe,
I gotta know if your sweet love is gonna save me.
We may lose and we may win, though we will never be here again,
So open up, I'm climbin' in, so take it easy.

3. Well, I'm a-runnin' down the road tryin' to loosen my load, got a world of trouble on my mind,
Lookin' for a lover who won't blow my cover, she's so hard to find.
Take it easy, take it easy.
Don't let the sound of your own wheels make you crazy.
Come on baby, don't say maybe,
I gotta know if your sweet love is gonna save me.

Hurdy Gurdy Man
Words and music by Donovan Leitch

Hur - dy gur - dy hur - dy gur - dy hur - dy gur - dy, gur - dy he sang ____

Hur - dy gur - dy hur - dy gur - dy hur - dy gur - dy gur - dy he sang ____

Hur - dy gur - dy hur - dy gur - dy hur - dy gur - dy, gur - dy he sang ____

Here comes the ro - ly po - ly man and he's sing - ing songs of love, ____

Repeat and fade

Ro - ly po - ly ro - ly po - ly po - ly ro - ly po - ly he sang. ____

Hey Jude
Words and music by John Lennon and Paul McCartney

cool by mak-ing his world a lit-tle cold-er, Da da da

da da da da da da da 3. Hey Jude don't let me down, you have

found her, now go and get her. Re-mem-ber to let her in-to your

heart, then you can start to make it bet-ter.

Fade

Woodstock
Words and music by Joni Mitchell

Suggested right hand pattern:

Moderately slow

Verse

1. I came up-on ____ a child of God; ___ he was walk-ing a-long ___ the road, and I asked him, "Where are you go - ing?" ___ and this he told me. "I'm go-ing on down ___ to Yas-gur's farm, ___ I'm gon-na join in a rock - and - roll

band.___ I'm gon-na camp out on the land, I'm gon-na try and get my

soul free." We are

Chorus

star - dust, we are gold - en, and we

got to get our - selves back to the gar -

1. 2.   3.

den.___ 2. "Then ___

2. "Then can I walk beside you? I have come here to lose the smog,
   And I feel to be a cog in something turning.
   Well, maybe it is just the time of year, or maybe it's the time of man.
   I don't know who I am, but life is for learning."
   (Chorus)

3. By the time we got to Woodstock we were half a million strong,
   And everywhere was song and celebration.
   And I dreamed I saw the bombers riding shotgun in the sky,
   And they were turning into butterflies above our nation.
   (Chorus)

23

Don't Be Cruel (To A Heart That's True)

Words and music by Otis Blackwell and Elvis Presley

Medium Bright (*with good beat*)

You know I can be found sit-ting home all a - lone If you can't come a -
Ba-by, if I made you mad for some-thing I might have said — Please let's for-get the

round, At least, please tel - e-phone. DON'T BE CRUEL _____ to a heart that's true. _____
past The fu-ture looks bright a-head. DON'T BE CRUEL _____ to a heart that's

true. _____ I don't want no oth-er love, Ba-by, it's just you I'm think-ing of. _____

Don't stop think-ing of me, Don't make me feel this way, Come on o-ver here and love me, You
walk up to the preach-er, and let us say, "I do." Then you'll know you have me, And I'll

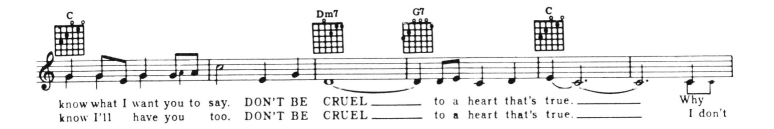

know what I want you to say. DON'T BE CRUEL _____ to a heart that's true. _____ Why
know I'll have you too. DON'T BE CRUEL _____ to a heart that's true. _____ I don't

should we be a-part? I real-ly love you, ba-by, cross my heart. _____ Let's
want no oth-er love, Baby, it's just you I'm think-ing

of. _____ DON'T BE CRUEL _____ to a heart that's true. _____ DON'T BE CRUEL _____ to a heart that's

true. _____ I don't want no oth-er love Ba-by, it's just you I'm think-ing of _____

Crocodile Rock

Words and music by Elton John and Bernie Taupin

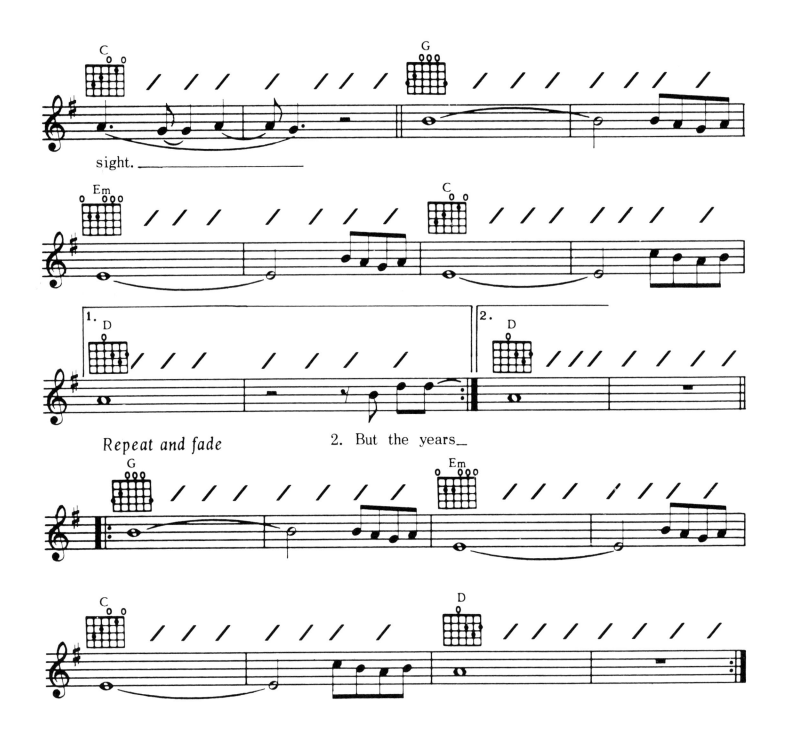

sight.

Repeat and fade   2. But the years___

2. But the years went by and rock just died,
   Susie went and left me for some foreign guy.
   Long nights cryin' by the record machine,
   Dreamin' of my Chevy and my old blue jeans.
   But they'll never kill the thrills we've got
   Burning up to the Crocodile Rock;
   Learning fast as the weeks went past,
   We really thought the Crocodile Rock would last.
                    (Chorus)

Get Back

Words and music by John Lennon and Paul McCartney

Sweet Loretta Modern thought she was a woman,
But she was another man.
All the girls around her said she's got it coming,
But she gets it while she can.

Get back! Get back!
Get back to where you once belonged.
Get back! Get back!
Get back to where you once belonged.

Brown Sugar

Moderate tempo (32 bars per minute)

Gold Coast slave ship bound for cot-ton fields, sold
Beat-ing, cold Eng-lish blood runs hot, la-
I bet your ma-ma was a Tent show queen, and

in a mar-ket down in New Or-leans. Scarred
-dy of the house won-d'rin where it's gon-na stop. House
all her girl friends were sweet six-teen. I'm

old slav-er know he's do-in' al-right. Hear
boy knows that he's do-in' al-right. You
no school boy but I know what I like. You

him whip the wo-men just a-round mid-night. Ah (2nd)
should a heard him just a-round mid-night.
should have heard me just

Brown Su-gar how come you taste so good (A-ha)

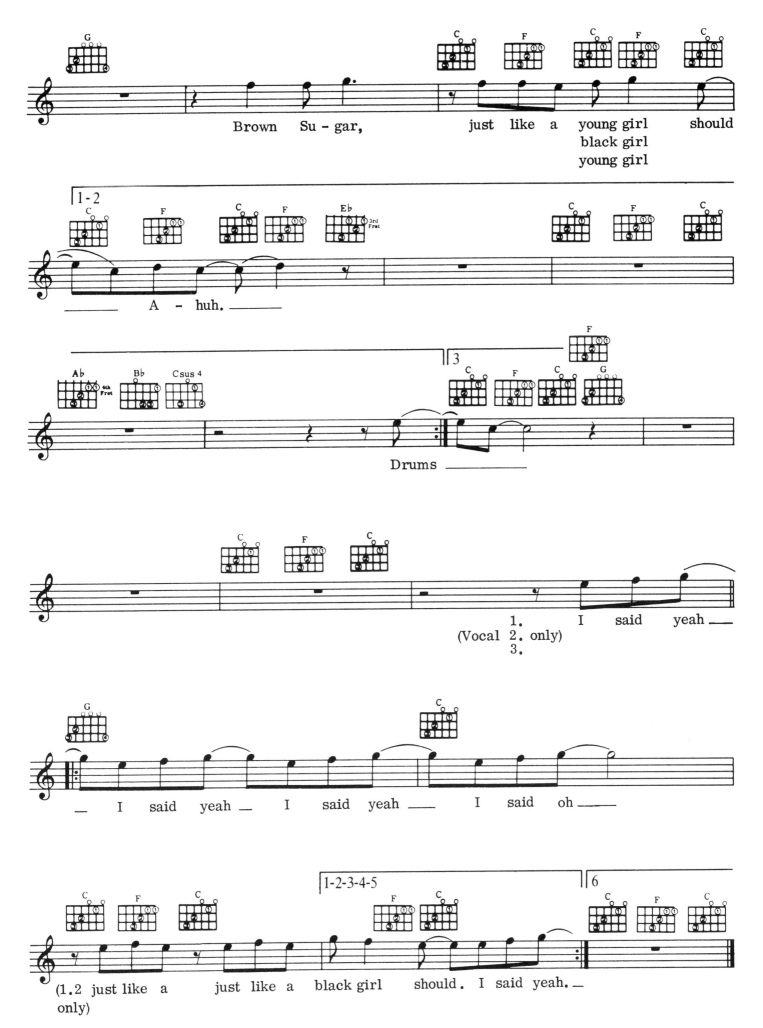

31

You're So Vain
Words and music by Carly Simon

Moderately

Verse

1. You walked in - to the par - ty like you were walk-ing on - to___ a yacht, your hat stra - te - gi - c'lly dipped be - low one eye, your scarf, it was ap - ri - cot. You had one eye in the mir - ror as you watched your - self___ ga - votte, and all the girls___ dreamed that they'd be your part - ner, they'd be your part - ner. And

Chorus

2. You had me several years ago when I was still quite naive.
   Well, you said that we make such a pretty pair, and that you would never leave.
   But you gave away the things you loved, and one of them was me.
   I had some dreams; they were clouds in my coffee, clouds in my coffee.
   (Chorus)

3. Well, I hear you went up to Saratoga and your horse naturally won.
   Then you flew your Lear jet up to Nova Scotia to see the total eclipse of the sun.
   Well, you're where you should be all the time and when you're not you're with
   Some underworld spy or the wife of a close friend, wife of a close friend.
   (Chorus)

California Girls
Words and music by Brian Wilson

Medium Rock

1. Well, East coast girls are hip. I real - ly
2. West coast has the sun - shine, and the

dig those styles they wear; __ And the South - ern girls __ with __ the
girls all get so tanned; __ I dig a French bi - ki - ni on Ha -

way they talk, __ They knock me out when I'm down there. __ The
wai - ian Is - lands, Dolls by a palm tree in the sand. __ I

mid - west farm - er's daugh - ters real - ly make you feel al -
been all a - round this great big world and I've seen all kinds of

right, __ And __ North - ern girls __ with __ the
girls, __ But I could - n't wait __ to __ get

way they kiss __ They keep their boy - friends warm at night. __ I
back in the states, __ Back to the cut - est girls in the world. __ I

34

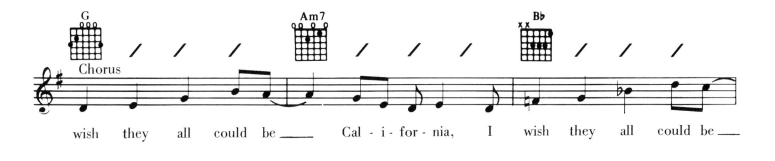

Chorus

wish they all could be ____ Cal - i - for - nia, I wish they all could be ____

____ Cal - i - for - nia, I wish they all could be ____ Cal - i - for - nia

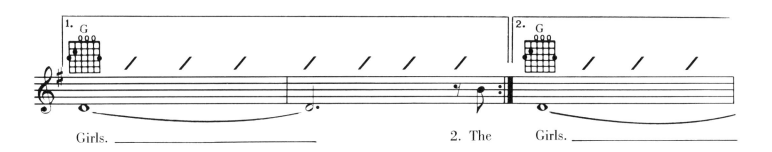

1. G

Girls. _____

2. G

2. The Girls. _____

Guitar Lead

____

I

G

wish they all could be ____ Cal - i - for - nia, I

Repeat and fade

C

wish they all could be ____ Cal - i - for - nia; I

Bad Moon Rising

Words and music by John C. Fogerty

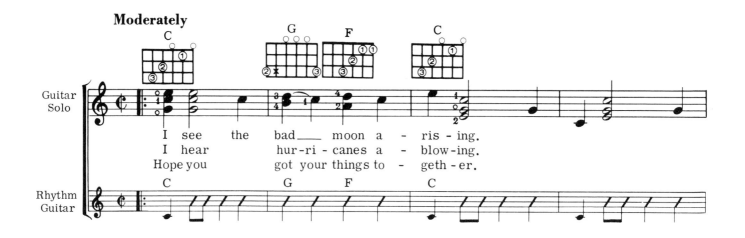

I see the bad__ moon a - ris - ing.
I hear hur-ri-canes a - blow-ing.
Hope you got your things to - geth - er.

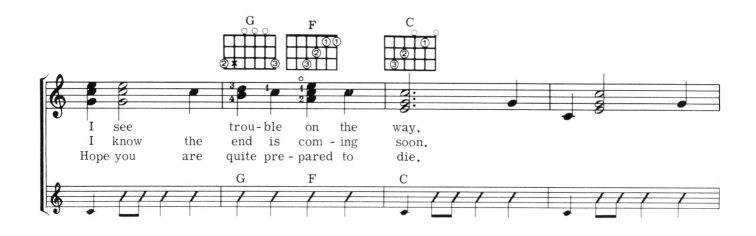

I see trou-ble on the way.
I know the end is com-ing soon.
Hope you are quite pre-pared to die.

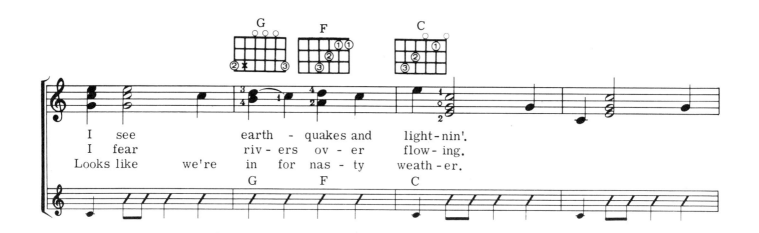

I see earth - quakes and light-nin'.
I fear riv-ers ov - er flow-ing.
Looks like we're in for nas-ty weath-er.

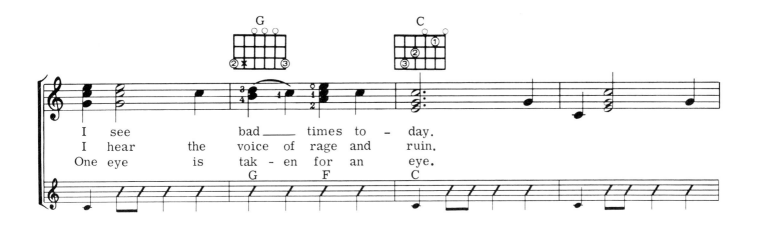

I see bad____ times to - day.
I hear the voice of rage and ruin.
One eye is tak - en for an eye.

Don't go a round to - night,____ Well, it's bound to take your

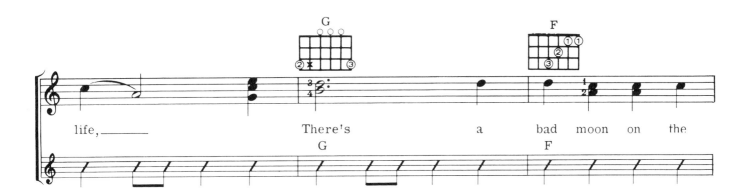

life,_____ There's a bad moon on the

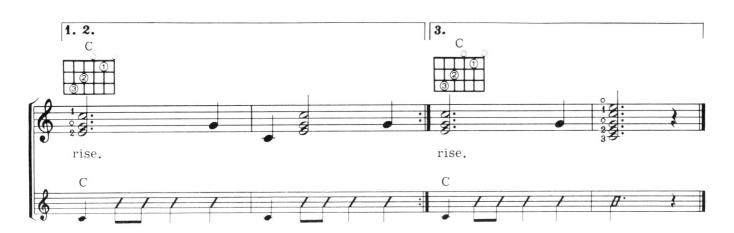

rise. rise.

That'll Be The Day

Words and music by Jerry Allison, Buddy Holly and Norman Petty

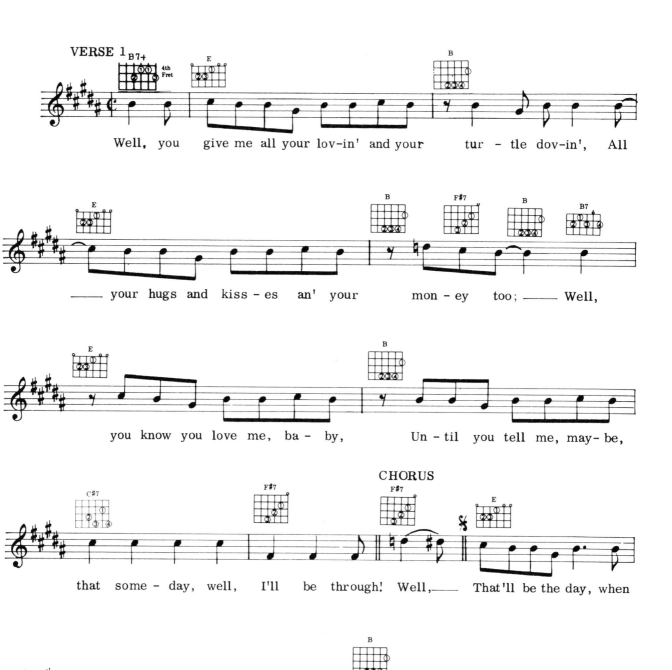

VERSE 1

Well, you give me all your lov-in' and your tur-tle dov-in', All ____ your hugs and kiss-es an' your mon-ey too; ____ Well, you know you love me, ba-by, Un-til you tell me, may-be,

CHORUS

that some-day, well, I'll be through! Well,____ That'll be the day, when you say, good-bye, Yes, ____ That-'ll be the day, when

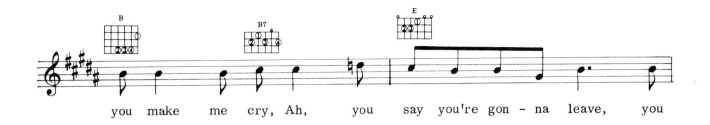

you make me cry, Ah, you say you're gon - na leave, you

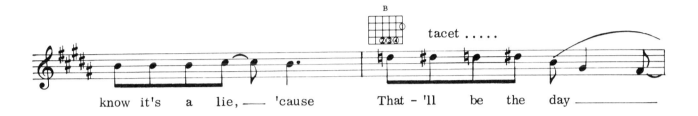

know it's a lie, ___ 'cause That -'ll be the day ___

1 *To Verse 2* **2** *Fine*

___ when I die. ___ Well, ___ when I die. ___

VERSE 2

When Cu - pid shot his dart, He shot it at your heart,

So if we ev - er part and I leave you, You say you told me an' you

To Chorus

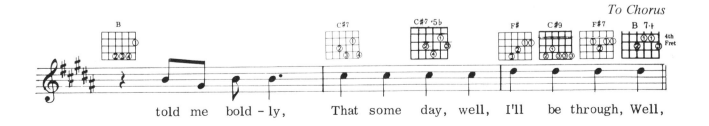

told me bold - ly, That some day, well, I'll be through, Well,

Both Sides Now

Words and music by Joni Mitchell

Moderately

1. Bows and flows of an-gel hair, and ice-cream cas - tles
2. Moons and Junes and Fer -ris wheels, the diz-zy danc-ing
3. Tears and fears and feel-ing proud, to say " I love you"

in the air, and feath-er can -yons ev -'ry - where, I've looked at clouds that
way you feel, as ev -'ry fai - ry tale comes real, I've looked at love that
right out loud, Dreams and schemes and cir-cus crowds, I've looked at life that

way. But now they on - ly block the sun, they rain and snow on
way. But now it's just an - oth-er show, you leave 'em laugh-ing
way. But now old friends are act -ing strange, they shake their heads, they

ev - 'ry one. So man - y things I would have done, But clouds got in my
when you go. And if you care don't let them know Don't give your-self a -
say I've changed. But some-thing's lost but some-thing's gained, In liv - ing ev - 'ry

way.
way. I've looked at clouds from both sides now from up and down and
day. I've looked at love from both sides now from give and take and
       I've looked at life from both sides now from win and lose and

still some - how it's cloud il - lu - sions I re-call, I real - ly don't know
still some - how it's love's il - lu - sions I re-call, I real - ly don't know
still some - how it's life's il - lu - sions I re-call, I real - ly don't know

clouds   at   all.
love   at   all.
life   at   all.

Everybody's Got Something To Hide
Except Me And My Monkey

Words and music by John Lennon and Paul McCartney

Moderately

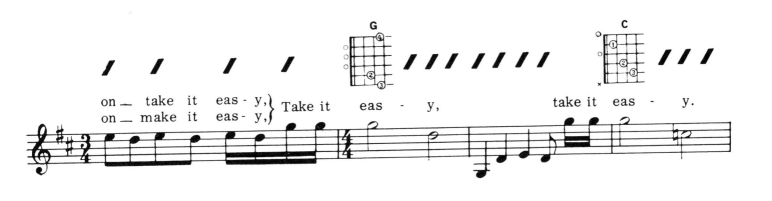

on — take it eas - y, }
on — make it eas - y, } Take it eas - y, take it eas - y.

Ev-'ry - bod- y's got some-thing to hide ex- cept for me and my

(hold)

mon- key.   *last time, end here*   The deep- er you go, the
                                              Your in - side is out, and your

high- er you fly; —— The high- er you fly, the deep- er you go, So come
out- side is in; —— Your out- side is in, and your in - side is out, So come

43

A Horse With No Name
Words and music by Dewey Bunnell

2. After nine days I let the horse run free 'cause the desert had turned to sea,
   There were plants and birds and rocks and things, there were sand and hills and rings.
   The ocean is a desert with its life underground and the perfect disguise above,
   Under the cities lies a heart made of ground, but the humans will give no love.
   (Chorus)

3. After two days in the desert sun my skin began to turn red,
   After three days in the desert fun I was looking at a river bed.
   And the story it told of a river that flowed made me sad to think it was dead.
   (Chorus)

45

Another Saturday Night
Words and music by Sam Cooke

A - noth - er   Sat - ur - day   night ___ and   I   ain't got   no - bod - y ;

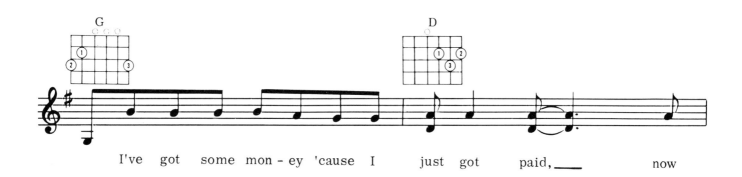

I've got   some   mon - ey   'cause I   just   got   paid, ___   now

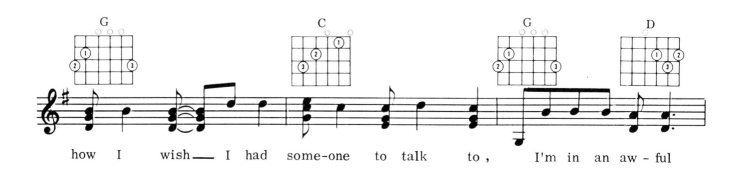

how   I   wish ___ I   had   some-one   to   talk   to ,   I'm in an aw - ful

way.   I   got   in   town   a

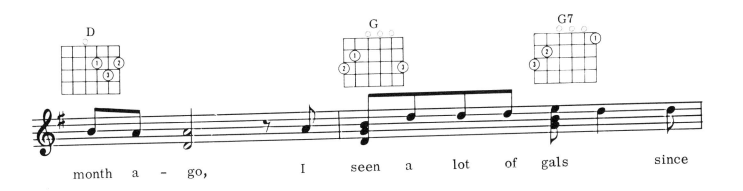

month a - go,   I   seen   a   lot   of   gals   since

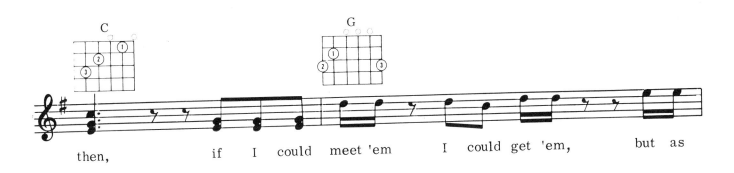

then,   if   I   could   meet 'em   I   could get 'em,   but as

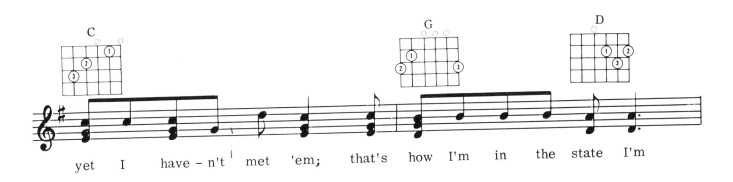

yet   I   have - n't   met 'em;   that's   how   I'm   in   the   state   I'm

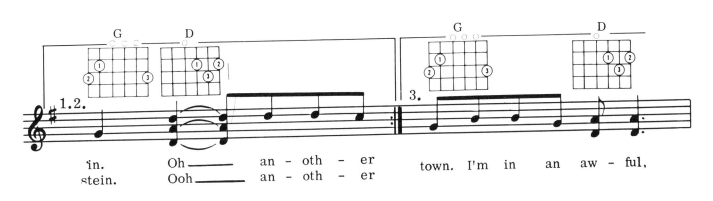

1.2.   'in.   Oh_____ an - oth - er   town. I'm   in   an   aw - ful,
       stein.   Ooh_____ an - oth - er

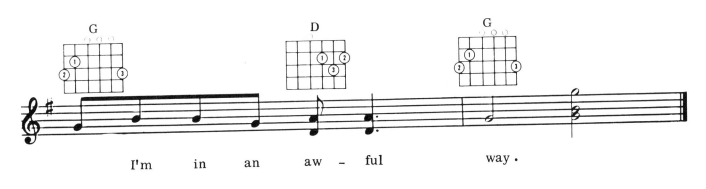

I'm   in   an   aw - ful   way.

Tequila Sunrise
Words and music by Glenn Frey and Don Henley

Bitch

Words and music by Mick Jagger and Keith Richard

30 bars per minute

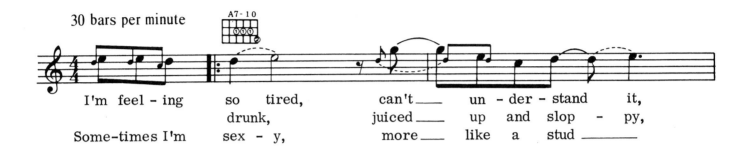

I'm feel-ing so tired, can't__ un-der-stand it,
drunk, juiced__ up and slop-py,
Some-times I'm sex-y, more__ like a stud __

Just had a fort-night's sleep,__ I'm feel-ing so tired. Ow!__
Ain't touched a drink__ all night,__ feel-ing hung-ry. Can't__
Kick-ing the stall__ all night,__ some-times I'm so shy. Got__

so dis-tract-ed, ain't touched a thing__ all week.
see the rea-son, just had a horse__ meat pie.__
to be worked__ on, don't have no bark__ or bite.__

[1] [2]

__ Feel-ing _____ Yeah__ when you call __

50

__ my name __ I sal - i - vate like a Pav - lov dog. ___

Yeah when you lay __ me out, __ my heart is beat-ing loud-er than a

Fine

big bass drum. ____ Yeah _ you _

_ got to mix __ it child, ya ___ got to fix __ it must be

love. _ It's a bitch, you _____ got to mix _ it child, _

D.C. al Fine

Ya got to fix __ it must be love. _ It's a bitch all right.

Red House
Words and music by Jimi Hendrix

There's a   red house   o - ver yon - der,   that's where my ___ ba - by

stays.   There's a   red house ___ o - ver yon - der, ba - by,

that's where   my ___ ba - by stays.   Well I

ain't been home to see   my ba - by   in a - bout a nine - ty nine and one half

days,   'Bout time I see her,   wait a min - ute,   some - thing's wrong,

The key won't un - lock the   door. ___   Wait a

Bad Bad Leroy Brown

Words and music by Jim Croce

Michelle

Words and music by John Lennon and Paul McCartney

Moderately

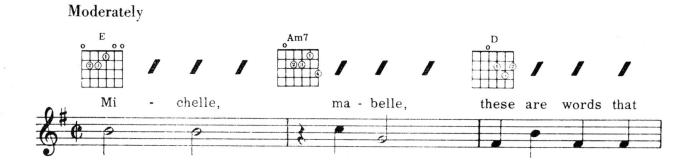

Mi - chelle, ma - belle, these are words that

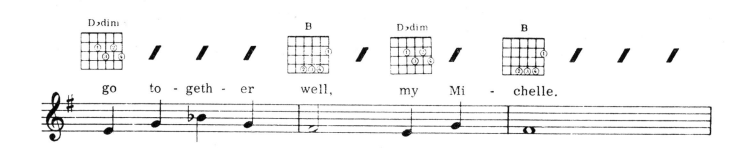

go to - geth - er well, my Mi - chelle.

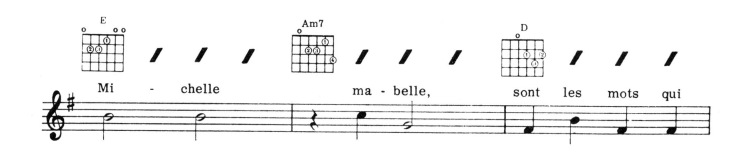

Mi - chelle ma - belle, sont les mots qui

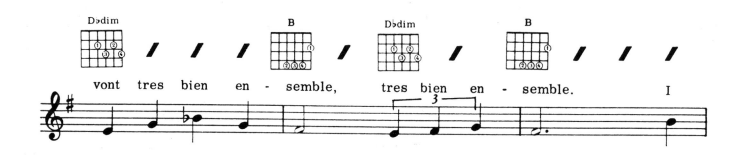

vont tres bien en - semble, tres bien en - semble. I

Michelle, ma belle, sont les mots qui vont tres bien ensemble, tres bien ensemble.
I need to, I need to, I need to, I need to make you see
Oh, what you mean to me.   Until I do I'm hoping you will know what I mean.

I want you, I want you, I want you, I think you know by now
I'll get to you somehow.   Until I do, I'm telling you so you'll understand,
My Michelle.

California Dreaming
Words and music by John Phillips

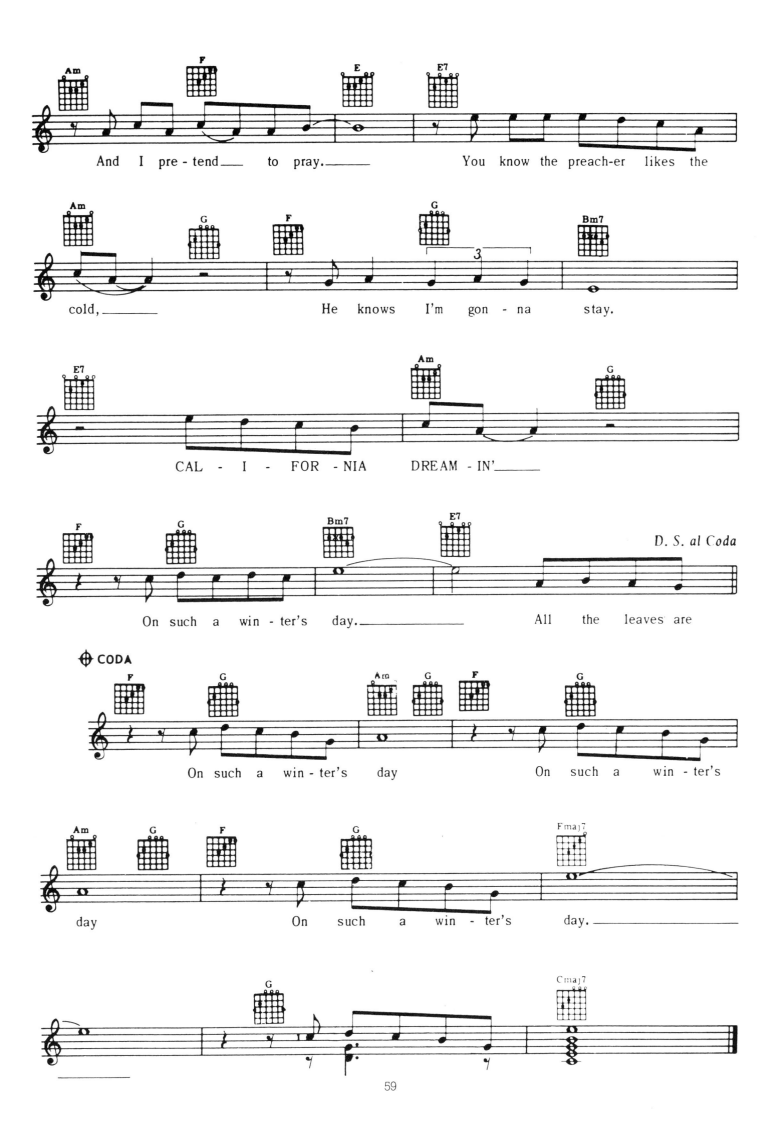

Help Me Ronda

Words and music by Brian Wilson

Medium Rock

1. Since she put me down I've been out do-in' in my head, ___
2. gon-na be my wife and I was gon-na be her man, ___

Come in late at night ___ and in the morn-in' I just lay in bed; ___
But she let an-oth-er guy come be-tween us and it ruined our plans; ___

Well, Ron-da you look ___ so
Well, Ron-da you caught ___ my

fine, _____ and I know it would-n't take much time, ___ For you to
eye, _____ and I'll give you lots of rea-sons why, ___ You got-ta

help me, Ron-da, Help me get her out of my heart. ___

Chorus

Help me, Ron - da! Help, help me, Ron - da! Help me, Ron - da!

Help, help me, Ron - da! Help me, Ron - da! Help, help me, Ron - da!

Help me, Ron - da! Help, help me, Ron - da! Help me, Ron - da!

Help, help me, Ron - da! Help me, Ron - da! Help, help me, Ron - da!

1.

Help me, Ron - da! Yeah, get her out of my heart.____

2.

2. She was ____ Help me, Ron - da!

Repeat and fade

Help, help me, Ron - da! Help me, Ron - da! Help, help me, Ron - da!

Words Of Love
Words and music by Buddy Holly

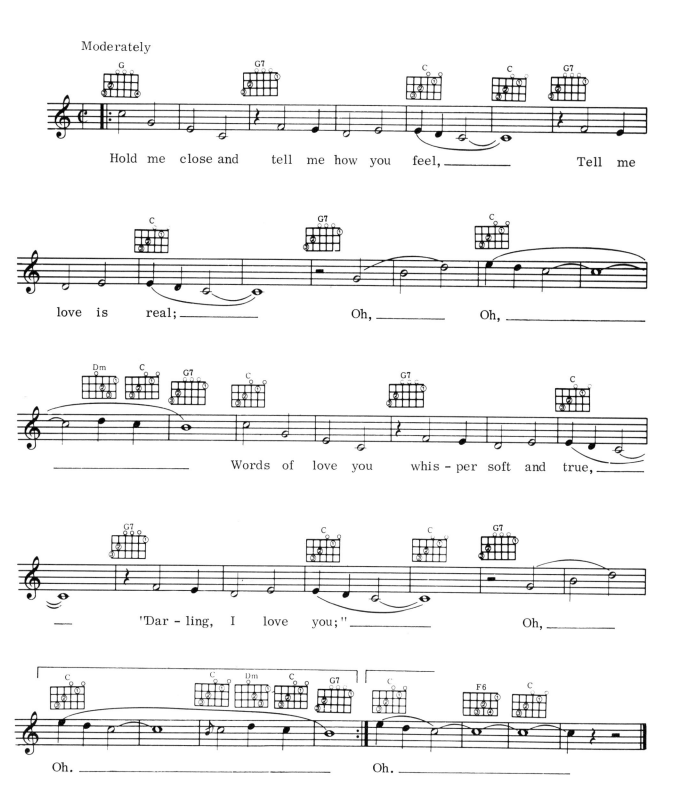

Warm Love

Words and music by Van Morrison

Moderately slow

Verse

1. Look at the i - vy on the old cling-ing wall, —

look at the flow - ers and the green grass so tall. —

It's not a mat - ter of when push comes to shove, —

it's just the hour — on the wings of a dove. That's just

warm — love, — it's just

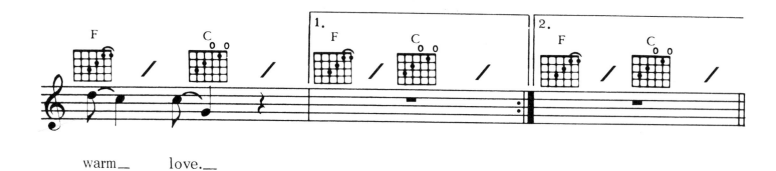

warm__ love.__

Chorus

And it's ev-er-pres-ent ev-'ry-where, and it's ev-er-pres-ent ev-'ry-where, that

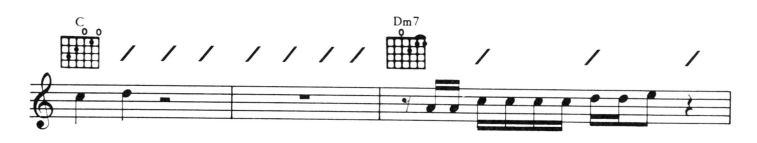

warm love. And it's ev-er-pres-ent ev-'ry-where,

To Coda ⊕

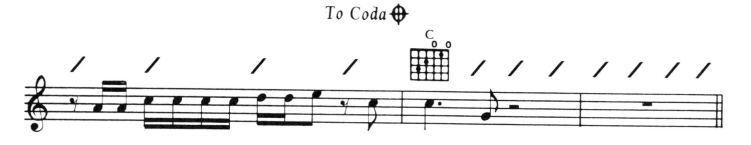

and it's ev-er-pres-ent ev-'ry-where, that warm love.

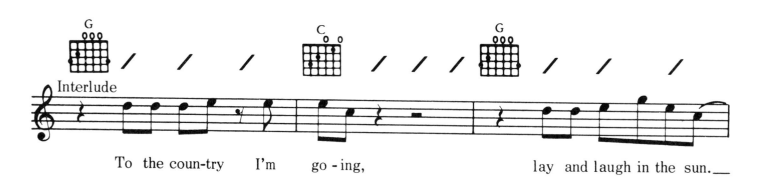

Interlude

To the coun-try I'm go-ing, lay and laugh in the sun.__

You can bring your gui - tar a -long, we'll

D. C. (no repeats) al Coda ⊕

sing some songs____ and have some fun. _____

Coda
⊕

warm love.

Verse 2. I dig it when you're fancy, dressed up in lace,
I dig it when you have a smile on your face.
This inspiration's got to be on the flow,
This invitation's got to see it and know.
It's just warm love,
It's just warm love.
(Chorus and Interlude)

Verse 3. The sky is crying and it's time to go home,
And we shall hurry to the car from the foam.
Sit by the fire and dry out our wet clothes,
It's raining outside from the skies up above.
Inside it's warm love,
Inside it's warm love.
(Chorus)

Bulbs
Words and music by Van Morrison

Moderately

1. I'm kick-ing off from cen-ter field, _____ a ques-tion of be-ing down for the game. The one-shot deal _ don't mat-ter, and the oth-er one's the same. Oh, my friend I

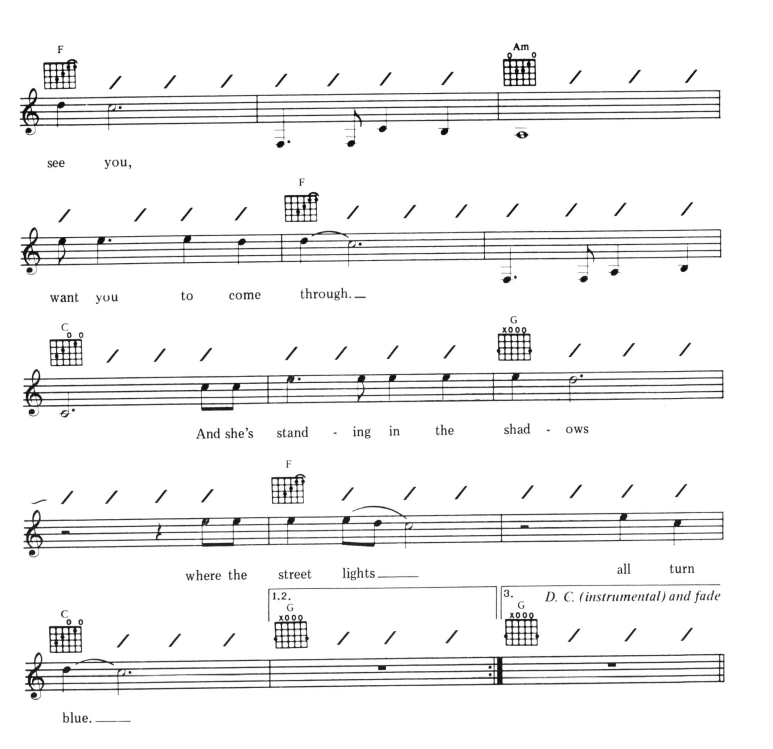

see you,

want you to come through. ——

And she's stand - ing in the shad - ows

where the street lights ——— all turn

blue. ———

2. She's leaving for an American, suitcase in her hand.
   Her brothers and her sisters are all on Atlantic sand.
   She's screaming through the alleyway, I hear the lonely cry, why can't you?
   And her batteries are corroded and her hundred-watt bulb just blew.

3. She used to hang out down at Miss Lucy's; every weekend they would get loose.
   And it was a straight, clear case of having taken in too much juice.
   It was outside and it was outside, just the nature of the person.
   Now all you gotta remember, after all it's all show biz.

Blue Suede Shoes

Words and music by Carl Lee Perkins

Bright tempo (not too fast)

CHORUS

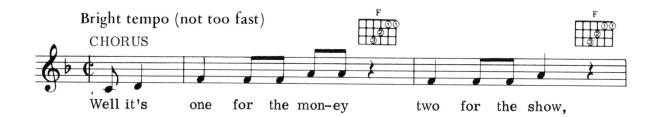

Well it's one for the mon-ey two for the show,

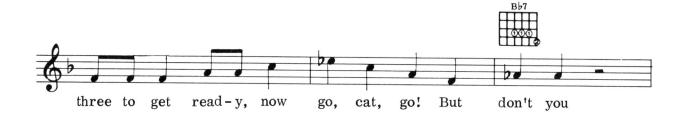

three to get read-y, now go, cat, go! But don't you

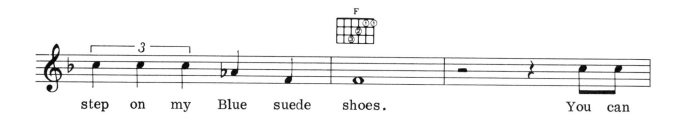

step on my Blue suede shoes. You can

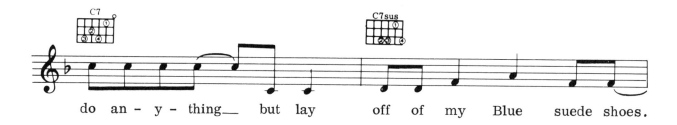

do an-y-thing__ but lay off of my Blue suede shoes.

Well, you can knock me down,
Burn my house,

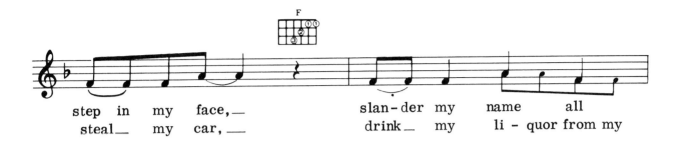

step in my face,— slan-der my name all
steal— my car,— drink— my li - quor from my

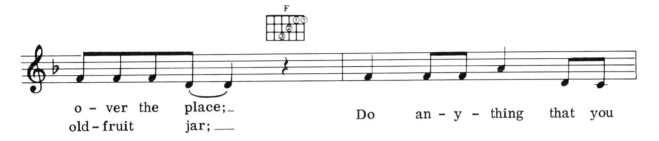

o - ver the place;— Do an - y - thing that you
old - fruit jar;—

want to do,— but uh - uh, hon-ey lay off of my shoes

Don't you step on my Blue suede shoes.

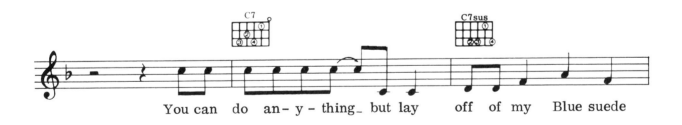

You can do an - y - thing— but lay off of my Blue suede

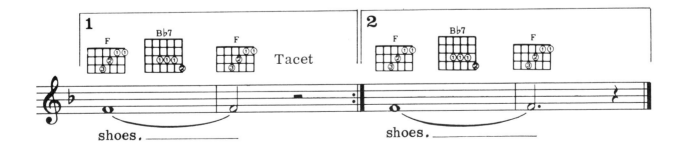

Tacet

1

shoes.————

2

shoes.————

Gimme Shelter

Words and music by Mick Jagger and Keith Richard

VERSE

1. Oh, _____ a storm ___ is threat' - ning, _____
2. See _____ the fire___ is sweep - ing, _____

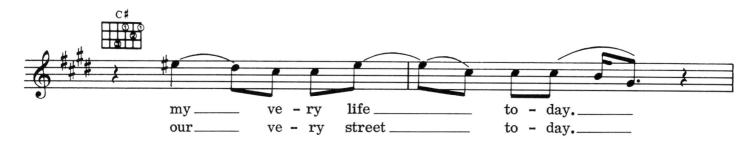

my _____ ve - ry life _____ to - day._____
our _____ ve - ry street _____ to - day.

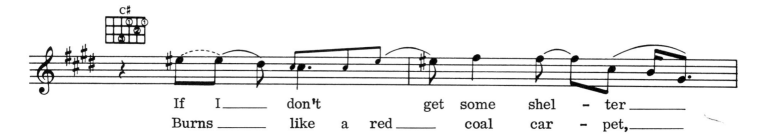

If I_____ don't get some shel - ter _____
Burns _____ like a red _____ coal car - pet,_____

Oh yeah ___ I'm gon - na fade___ a - way. _____
Mad _____ bull lost _____ it's way.

CHORUS

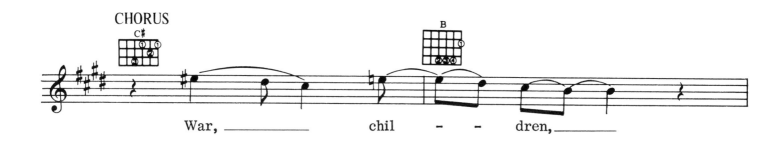

War, _____ chil - - dren,_____

It's just a shot a-way,___ It's just a shot a-way.___

War,_____ chil - dren, ___ It's just a shot a-way, ___

It's just a shot _ a - way.

way.

Rape,_ mur - der,_____ It's just a shot a-way,

It's just a shot a - way___ -ay - ay_ ay_____ ay.

Heart Of Gold
Words and music by Neil Young

Keep me search-in' for a heart of gold, _____
Keeps me search-in' for a heart of gold, _____

and I'm get-tin' old.
and I'm get-tin' old.

Keep me search-in' for a heart of gold, ___

you keep me search-in' and I'm grow-in' old. ___

Keep me search-in' for a heart of gold, __ I've been a min-er for a

heart of gold. _____

Paperback Writer

Words and music by John Lennon and Paul McCartney

un - der - stand.   His   son   is   work-ing   for the   Dail - y   Mail;   It's   a

stead - y   job,   but   he   wants to   be   a   pa - per - back

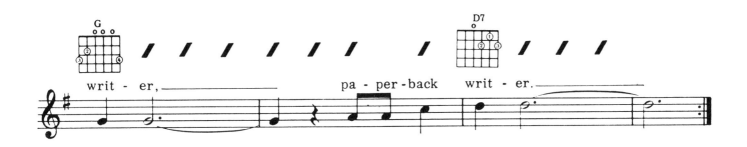

writ - er, _____   pa - per - back   writ - er. _____

It's a thousand pages, give or take a few,
I'll be writing more in a week or two.
I can make it longer if you like the style,
I can change it 'round and I want to be a paperback writer, paperback writer.
If you really like it you can have the rights,
It could make a million for you overnight.
If you must return it you can send it here;
But I need a break and I want to be a paperback writer, paperback writer

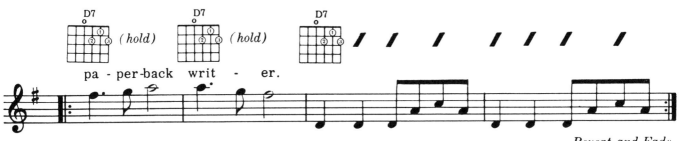

pa - per - back   writ -   er.

Repeat and Fade

Walk On By

Words and music by Hal David and Burt Bacharach

Slowly

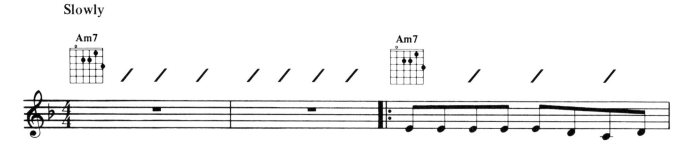

1. If you see me walk-in' down the
2. I just can't get o-ver los-in'
3. (Instrumental) _____

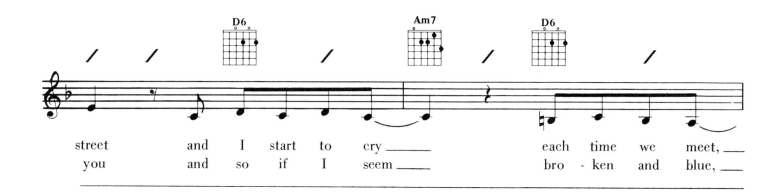

street   and   I   start   to   cry _____   each time   we   meet, __
you   and   so   if   I   seem ____   bro - ken   and   blue, __

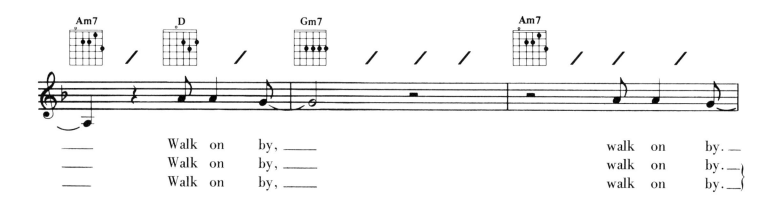

_____   Walk on   by, _____   walk   on   by. _
_____   Walk on   by, _____   walk   on   by. _
             Walk on   by, _____   walk   on   by. _

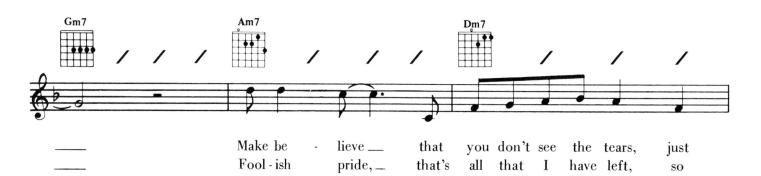

_____   Make be - lieve ___   that   you don't see the tears,   just
_____   Fool-ish   pride, _   that's all that   I   have left,   so

76

let   me   grieve ___   in   pri - vate,   'cause   each   time   I
let   me   hide ___   the   tears   and   the   sad - ness   you

see   you,   I   break   down   and   cry.
gave   when   you   said   good - bye.

Walk   on   by, ___   (don't   stop,)   walk   on   by, __

___   (don't   stop,)   walk   on   by. ___

___   (don't   stop,)   walk   on   by, __

Peggy Sue

Words and music by Jerry Allison, Buddy Holly and Norman Petty

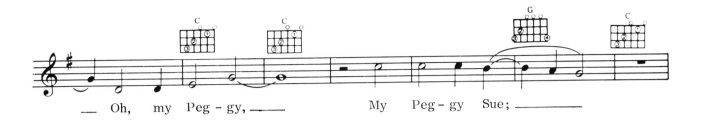

Oh, my Peg-gy, _____ My Peg-gy Sue; _____

Oh, well, I love you gal, and I need you, Peg-gy Sue.__

_____ I love you, __ Peg-gy Sue, __

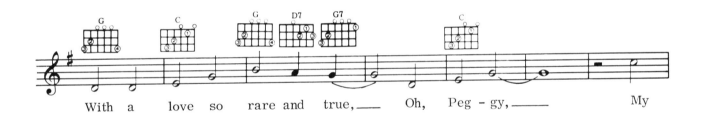

With a love so rare and true,__ Oh, Peg-gy, _____ My

Peg-gy Sue; _____ Oh, well, I love you gal,__ Yes, I want you,

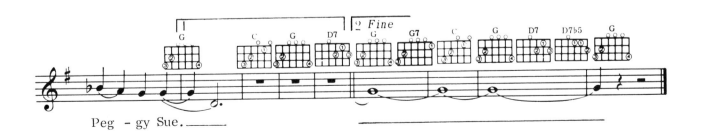

Peg - gy Sue._____

Tutti Frutti

Words and music by D. la Bostrie, Joe Lubin and Richard Penniman

Bright Rock 'n' Roll tempo

CHORUS

A - bop - bop - a - loom-op a - lop bop boom! Tut - ti

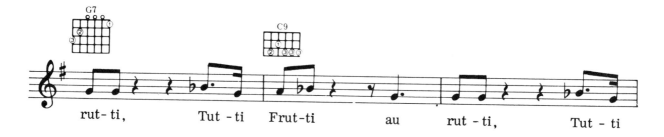

Frut-ti au rut - ti, Tut - ti Frut -ti au

rut- ti, Tut - ti Frut-ti au rut - ti, Tut - ti

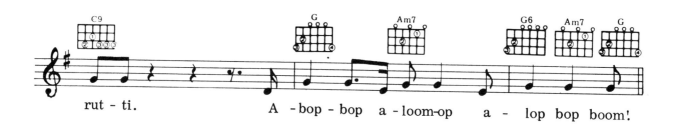

Frut - ti au rut - ti, Tut - ti Frut-ti au

rut - ti. A - bop - bop a - loom-op a - lop bop boom!

VERSE

I got a gal   her name's Sue   She
I got a gal   her name's Dai - sy   She
I got - ta go,   can't stop,
You're the one   I miss,   I
Won't you be   my date,   And

knows just what to do ____   I got a gal   her name's
al - most drives me cra - zy   I got a gal   her name's
Down to the can - dy shop ____   I got - ta go,   can't
got - ta tell you this ____   Oh, you're the one   I
ba - by, don't be late ____   Oh, won't you be   my

Sue,   She knows just what to do. ____   I've
Dai - sy   She al - most drives me cra - y   She's a
stop,   And get me an ice - cream pop. ____
miss,   And the fla - vor of your kiss. ____   I
date,   And share my ice - cream plate. ____   With-

been to the east,   I've been to the west,   but
real gone cook-ie,   yes - sir - ree,   but
Don't want va - nil - la or straw- ber - ry too,   Want the
don't mean cher-ry with choc-'late chips,   I
-out your kiss-es,   this is all I've got,   just an

she's the the gal I love the best.
pret - ty lit - lte Su - zy's the gal for me.
same kind of fla - vor when I'm kiss-ing you. Tut - ti
mean the same fla - vor of your sweet lips.
im - i - ta - tion fla - vor of you know what.

CHORUS

Frut- ti au rut-ti Tut - ti Frut-ti au

rut - ti Tut - ti Frut - ti au rut - ti Tut - ti

Frut-ti au rut-ti Tut-ti Frutti au rut-ti A

1
bop-bop a-loom-op a - lop bop boom! 2.I got a
3. I got a
4. You're the
5. Won't you lop bop boom!

82

Morning Has Broken

Words and music by Eleanor Farjeon and Cat Stevens

Love The One You're With

Words and music by Stephen Stills

ea - gle flies with the dove;— and if you

can't be with the one you love,— hon -ey,

love the one— you're with, love the one— you're with,

love the one— you're with,

love the one— you're with. 2. Don't be

2. Don't be angry, don't be sad,
   And don't sit cryin' over good times you've had.
   There's a girl right next to you
   And she's just waitin' for something to do.
   And there's a rose (etc.)

3. Turn your heartache right into joy;
   She's a girl and you're a boy.
   Well, get it together, make it nice;
   You ain't gonna need any more advice.
   And there's a rose (etc.)

Tumbling Dice

Words and music by Mick Jagger and Keith Richard

Moderate Rock

Wom - en think I'm tas - ty, but they're al - ways try-in' to waste me and make

__ me burn the can - dle right down, _____ but ba - by, __

ba - by, __ I don't need no jew-els in my crown. __ "Cause all __

__ you wom - en is low __ down gam - blers, cheat - in' like I don't know how, __

__ but ba - by, __ ba - by, __ there's

fe - ver in the funk house now. _____ This low down bitch- in' got my __

poor feet a-itch-in', you know,__ you know the deuce is still wild.

Ba - by,__ I can't stay,__ you got to roll__ me and

call me the tum - blin'__ dice._____ Al -

- ways in a hur-ry, I nev-er stop to wor-ry, don't__you see the time flash-in' by.__

Hon - ey, got no mon - ey,__ I'm all

six - es and sev - ens and nines.____ Say now, ba - by, I'm the

rank out - sid - er, you__ can be my part-ner in crime.____ But

ba - by, ___ I can't stay,_ you got to roll _____ me and

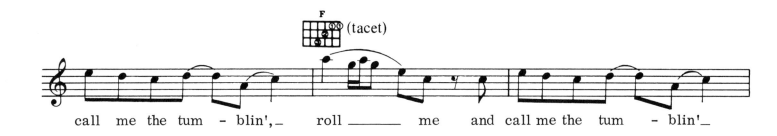

call me the tum - blin', _ roll _____ me and call me the tum - blin'_

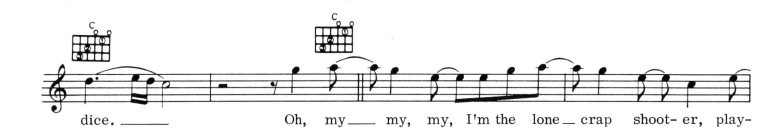

dice. _____ Oh, my ___ my, my, I'm the lone _ crap shoot- er, play-

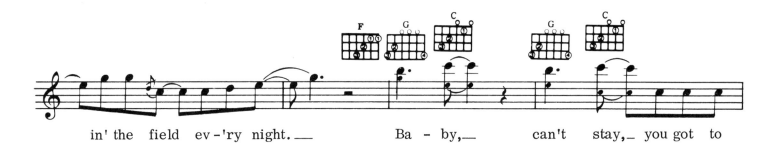

in' the field ev -'ry night. ___ Ba - by, ___ can't stay,_ you got to

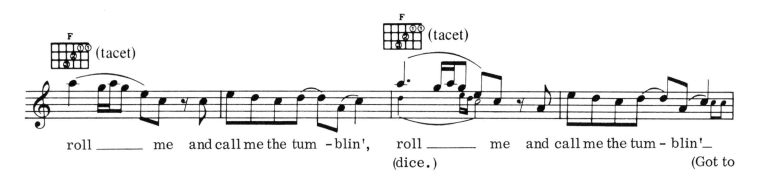

roll _____ me and call me the tum -blin', roll _____ me and call me the tum - blin'_

(dice.)   (Got to

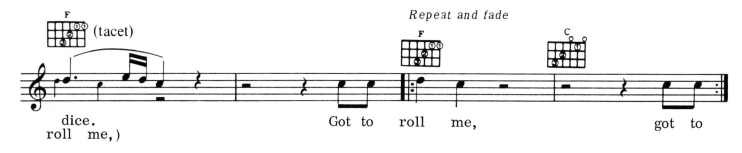

dice. ___ Got to roll me, got to

roll me,)

I Walk The Line

Words and music by John R. Cash

Starting note for singing:

Moderately

(No chord) **G7** I keep a close watch on this heart of mine, **C**

G7 I keep my eyes wide o-pen all the time, **C**

F I keep the ends out for the tie that binds, **C**

G7 Be- cause you're mine I walk the line. **C**

N.C. G7/ / / / / / /C / / / /
2. I find it very, very easy to be true,
/ / /G7 / / / / / / /C / / /
I find myself alone when each day is through,
/ / / F/ / / / / / / C / / / /
Yes, I'll admit that I'm a fool for you,
/ / / G7/ / / / / / / C / / / /
Because you're mine, I walk the line.

N.C. G7// / / / / / C / / / /
3. As sure as night is dark and day is light,
/ / / G7/ / / / / / / C / / /
I keep you on my mind both day and night,
/ / /F/ / / / / / / C / / / /
And happiness I've known proves that it's right.
/ / / G7/ / / // / / C / / / /
Because you're mine, I walk the line.

N.C. G7/// / / / / C / / / /
4. You've got a way to keep me on your side,
/ / / G7/ / / / / / C / / /
You give me cause for love that I can't hide,
/ / /F / / / / / / C / / / /
For you I know I'd even try to turn the tide,
/ / / G7/ / / // / / C / / / /
Because you're mine, I walk the line.

5. (Same as first verse)

89

Surfin' Safari

Words and music by Michael Love and Brian Wilson

Fast Rock

Let's go surf-in' now, ev-'ry-bod-y's learn-in' how,

come on a sa-fa-ri with me. _____

Ear-ly in the morn-ing we'll be start-in' out, ____ some
ang-lin' in La-gu-na and Cerro A zul, ____ they're

hon-eys will be com-in' a-long. _____ We're
kick-in' out in Do-he-ny too. _____ I tell you

load-in' up our wood-y with the boards in-side and
surf-in's run-nin' wild, it's get-tin' big-ger ev-'ry day from Ha-

head-in' out sing-in' our song. _____
wai-i to the shores of Pe ru. _____

90

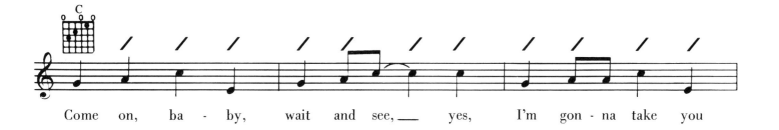

Come on, ba - by, wait and see, ___ yes, I'm gon - na take you

surf - in' with me. ___ Lone - some ba - by, wait and see, ___ yes,

I'm gon - na take you surf - in' with me. ___ Let's go surf - in' now,

To Coda ⊕

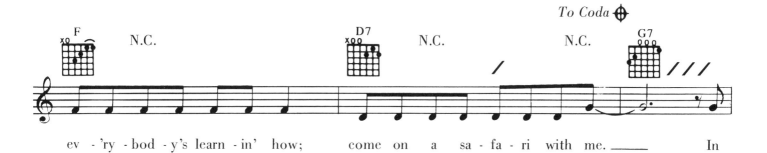

ev - 'ry - bod - y's learn - in' how; come on a sa - fa - ri with me. ___ In

Hunt - ing - ton and Ma - li - bu there shoot - in' the pier, ___ in Rin - con, they're walk - in' the nose.

___ We're go - in' on sa - fa - ri to the is - lands this year, ___ so if you're

com - in', get read - y to go._____ Come on, ba - by,

wait and see,__ yes, I'm gon - na take you surf - in' with me.__

Lone - some ba - by, wait and see,__ yes, I'm gon - na take you

surf - in' with me. __ Let's go surf - in' now, ev - 'ry - bod - y's learn - in' how;

come on a sa - fa - ri with me._____ They're

Coda

Repeat and fade

With me, yeh me with me

92

Diamonds And Rust

Words and music by Joan Baez

Moderately Fast

Guitar Intro

Well,

I'll be damned here comes your ghost a-gain. _____
I re-mem-ber your eyes were blu-er than rob-in's eggs. _____
you burst on the scene al-read-y a leg-end. _____
tell-ing me you're not nos-tal-gic. _____

_____ But that's not un-us-u-al; it's just that the
_____ My po-et-ry was lous-y you said. Where are you
_____ The un-washed phe-nom-e-non. The o-rig-i-nal
_____ Then give me an-oth-er word for it, you who're so

moon is full and you hap-pened to call.
call-ing from, a booth in the mid-west?
vag-a-bond, you strayed in-to my arms.
good with words and at keep-ing things vague.

93

And here I sit,   hand   on the
Ten years a - go   I bought   you some
And there you stayed   tem - po - rar - i - ly
'Cause I need some of that vague-ness now;   it's all   come   back too

C   G

tel - e - phone,   hear - ing a voice ____ I'd known
cuff - links;   you brought me some   thing.
lost at sea;   The ma - don - na was yours ____ for free.
clear - ly.   Yes, I loved you dear   ly.

D

a cou - ple of light ____ years a - go,   head - ing straight for a
We both know what mem - 'ries can bring: they bring dia - monds and
Yes, the girl on the half - shell   could keep you un -
And if you're of - f'ring me dia - monds and rust,   I've al - read - y

Em   *Last time to Coda* ⊕ | 1. 2. | 3.

fall.   As   Now I
rust.   Well,
harmed.
paid.

Bm

see you stand - ing with brown leaves   fall - ing all a - round and snow in your

94

hair.   Now you're smil - ing out the win - dow of that

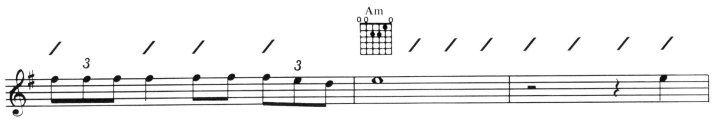

crum - my ho - tel   o - ver Wash-ing - ton   Square.   Our

breath comes out white clouds,   min - gles   and hangs   in the   air.

Speak-ing   strict - ly   for   me,   we   both could have died   then and

there. _____

D. S. 𝄋 al Coda ⊕

Now you're

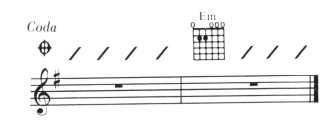

Coda
⊕

Sundown
Words and music by Gordon Lightfoot

Moderately, with a strong beat

1. I can see her ly - in' back in her sat - in dress in a

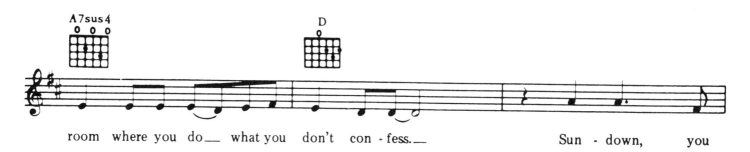

room where you do___ what you don't con - fess.___ Sun - down, you

bet - ter take care___ if I find you bin creep - in' round___ my back stairs.___

Sun - down, you bet - ter take care___ if I find you bin creep-in' round___

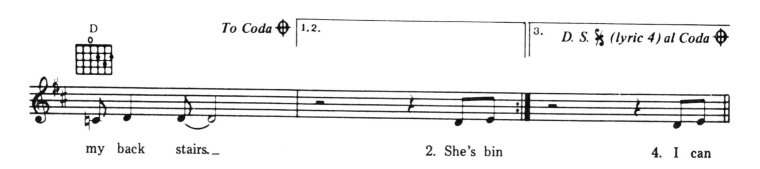

my back stairs. ___   2. She's bin   4. I can

96

Coda ⊕

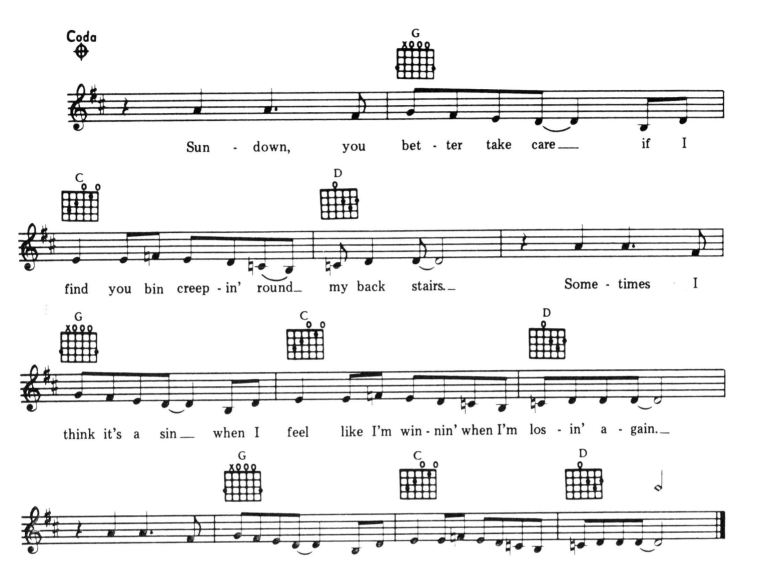

Sun - down, you bet - ter take care ___ if I

find you bin creep - in' round ___ my back stairs. ___ Some - times I

think it's a sin ___ when I feel like I'm win - nin' when I'm los - in' a - gain. ___

2. She's bin lookin' like a queen in a sailor's dream
   and she don't always say what she really means.
   Sometimes I think it's a shame when I get feelin' better when I'm feeling no pain.
   Sometimes I think it's a shame when I get feelin' better when I'm feeling no pain.

3. I can picture every move that a man could make;
   gettin' lost in her lovin' is your first mistake.
   Sundown, you better take care if I find you bin creepin' round my back stairs.
   Sometimes I think it's a sin when I feel like I'm winnin' when I'm losin' again.

4. I can see her lookin' fast in her faded jeans;
   she's a hard lovin' woman, got me feelin' mean.
   Sometimes I think it's a shame when I get feelin' better when I'm feelin' no pain.
   Sundown, you better take care if I find you been creepin' round my back stairs.
   Sundown, you better take care, etc.

All Shook Up

Words and music by Otis Blackwell and Elvis Presley

Medium Shuffle Rhythm

A - well - a, bless my soul,_ What's wrong with me?_ I'm
itch - ing like a man_ on a fuz - zy tree_ My
friends say I'm act - in' queer as a bug_ I'm in love I'm
All shook up!_ Mm mm oh, oh, yeah, yeah!_____
_ My hands are sha-ky and my knees are weak, I
can't seem to stand on my own two feet, Who do you thank when you

have such luck? I'm in love! I'm All shook up!_ Mm

Eb7   F7   Bb   Eb7   Bb

mm,   oh,   oh,   yeah,   yeah!_____

Eb7

1. Please don't ask what's on my mind, I'm a
2. Tongue gets tied when I try to speak, My__

Bb

lit - tle mixed up but I'm feel - in' fine__ When I'm
in - side shakes like a leaf on a tree, There's

Eb7

near__ that girl that__ I__ love best, My__
on - ly one cure for this soul of mine, That's to

F7   Opt.

heart beats so it__ scares me to death! She
have the girl that I love so fine!

99

Little Wing
Words and music by Jimi Hendrix

Pinball Wizard
Words and music by Peter Townshend

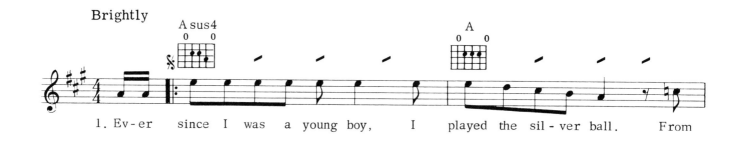

1. Ev-er since I was a young boy, I played the sil-ver ball. From

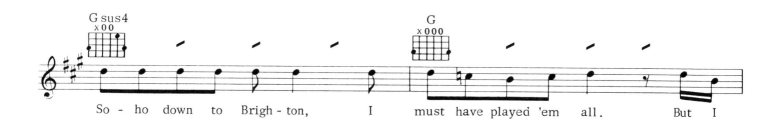

So-ho down to Brigh-ton, I must have played 'em all. But I

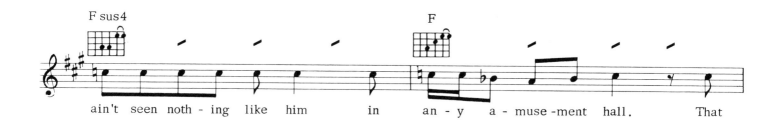

ain't seen noth-ing like him in an-y a-muse-ment hall. That

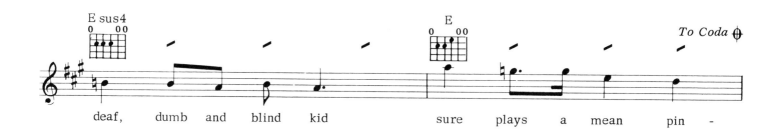

deaf, dumb and blind kid sure plays a mean pin-

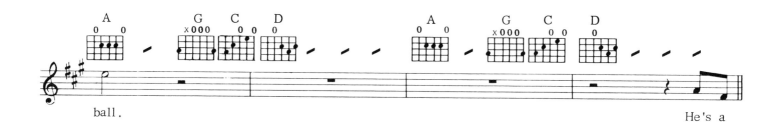

ball. He's a

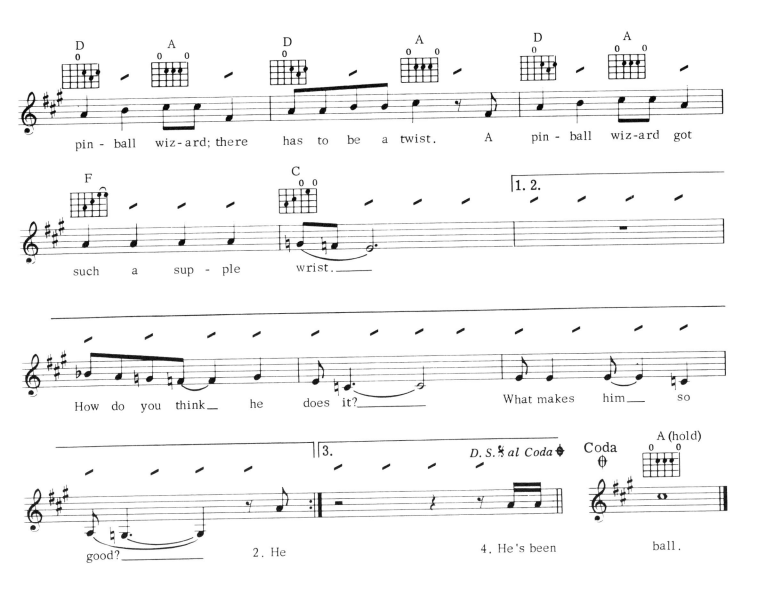

pin - ball wiz-ard; there has to be a twist. A pin - ball wiz-ard got

such a sup - ple wrist.

How do you think— he does it?_____ What makes him— so

good?_____ 2. He 4. He's been ball.

2. He stands like a statue, becomes part of the machine.
   Feeling all the bumpers, always playing clean.
   Plays by intuition; the digit counters fall.
   That deaf, dumb and blind kid sure plays a mean pinball.
   He's a pinball wizard (etc.)

3. Ain't got no distractions, can't hear no buzzers and bells.
   Don't see no lights a-flashin'; plays by sense of smell.
   Always gets a replay; never tilts at all.
   That deaf, dumb and blind kid sure plays a mean pinball.
   I thought I was the Bal-ly table king,
   But I just handed my pinball crown to him.

4. Even on my favorite table, he can beat my best.
   His disciples lead him in, and he just does the rest.
   He's got crazy, flippin' fingers; never seen him fall.
   That deaf, dumb and blind kid sure plays a mean pinball.

Instant Karma
Words and music by John Lennon

of? ___   Laugh-in' in the face of love, ___
see? ___   Laugh-in' at ___ fools like me, ___

C   **D**

what on earth you tryin' to do?   It's up to you!   Yeah
who on earth d'you think you are?   A su-per star?   Well, al -

1.   **2.**   𝄋

E7   **E7**   **G**   **Bm**   **Em**

you!   right you are! Well we all shine on ___ like the

G   **Bm**   **Em**   **G**   **Bm**

moon and the stars and the sun! ___   Yeh, we all shine

Em   **D**   **E7**

                                                          D.S. for fade

on, ___   ev-'ry-one,   come on!

Please Mr. Postman

Words and music by Brian Bert, Georgia Dobbins,
William Garrett and Freddie Gorman

Stop, oh yes, wait a min-ute Mis-ter Post-man.　　Wait, _____

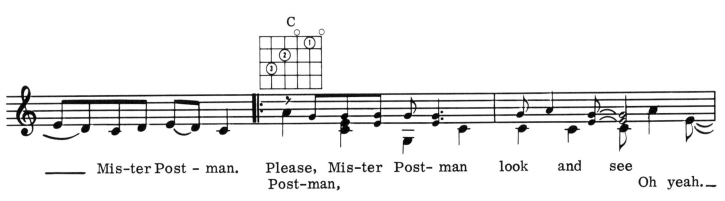

_____ Mis-ter Post-man.　Please, Mis-ter Post-man look and see
Post-man,　　　　　　　　　　　　　　　　　　　　　Oh yeah._

_____ is there a let-ter in your bag for me?_____
_____　　　　　　　　　　　　　　Please, _____ Mis-ter

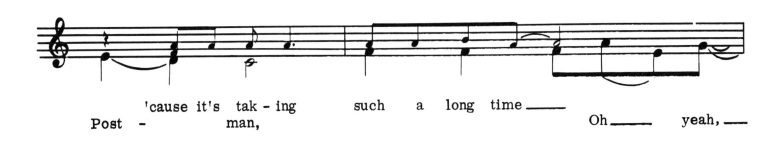

'cause it's tak-ing　such a long time _____
Post - man,　　　　　　　　　　　　　Oh _____ yeah, _____

_____ for me to hear from that boy of mine._____　There must _____ be some
　　　　　　　　　　　　　　　　　　　　　　　So man - y days　you

word to - day, _____ from my boy-friend   so far a - way.
F passed me by, _____ see the tears stand-ing in   my eyes.

Please, Mis - ter   Post - man   look   and   see, _____
G You did - n't   stop   to   make me feel   bet-ter

2nd time D.S.

if there's a let - ter,   a   let - ter for me? _____
by leav - ing me   a   card or a let - ter, Mis-ter

C
1.

I've been ____ stand-ing here ____ wait - ing Mis - ter Post - man,

Am

F so, so _____ pa - tient-ly, _____ for just a card

F   G

or just a let - ter,   say-ing he's re-turn-ing home__to me.__ Mis-ter

107

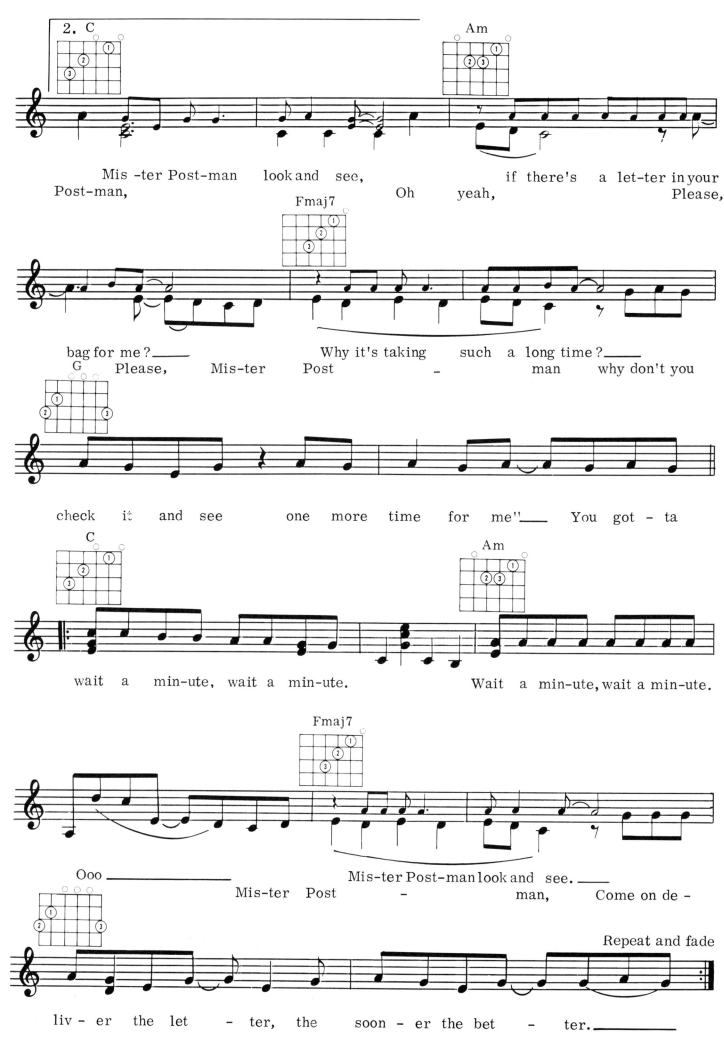

2. C   Am

Mis -ter Post-man   look and see,   if there's   a let-ter in your
Post-man,   Oh   yeah,   Please,

                                         Fmaj7

bag for me?_____   Why it's taking   such   a long time?_____
   G   Please,   Mis-ter   Post —   man   why don't you

check it and see   one more time for me"___ You got-ta

C   Am

wait a min-ute, wait a min-ute.   Wait   a min-ute, wait a min-ute.

                         Fmaj7

Ooo _____   Mis-ter Post-man look and see._____
            Mis-ter Post —   man,   Come on de -

                                                        Repeat and fade

liv- er the let — ter, the   soon- er the bet — ter._____

108

Jumpin' Jack Flash

Heartbeat
Words and music by Bob Montgomery and Norman Petty

Moderato

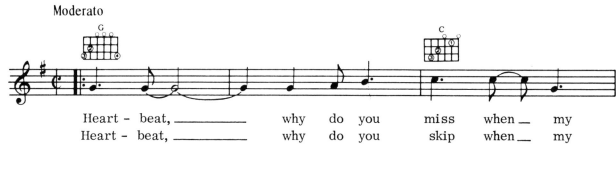

Heart - beat, _____ why do you miss when _ my
Heart - beat, _____ why do you skip when _ my

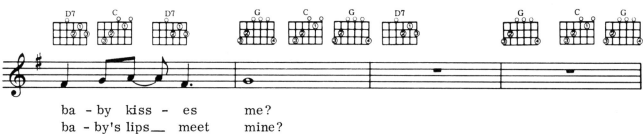

ba - by kiss - es me?
ba - by's lips _ meet mine?

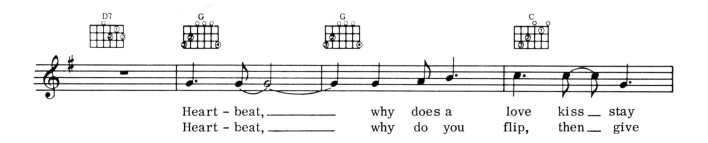

Heart - beat, _____ why does a love kiss _ stay
Heart - beat, _____ why do you flip, then _ give

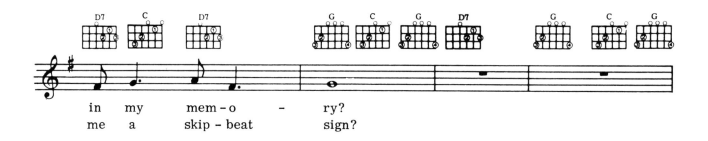

in my mem - o - ry?
me a skip - beat sign?

Rid- dle-dee-pat,— I know that new— love thrills me,—
Rid- dle -dee-pat,— and sing to me— love's sto - ry,—

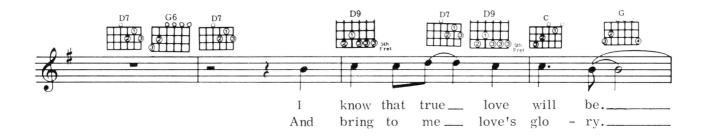

I know that true— love will be._____
And bring to me— love's glo - ry._____

_____ Heart - beat, why do you miss when my
_____ Heart - beat, why do you miss when my

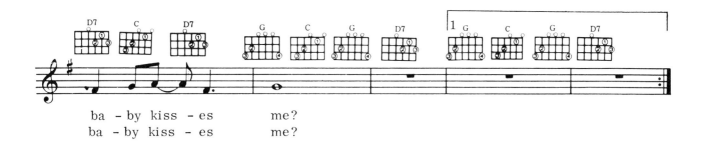

ba - by kiss - es me?
ba - by kiss - es me?

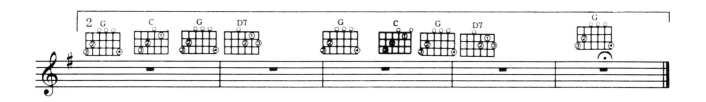

Eleanor Rigby

Words and music by John Lennon and Paul McCartney

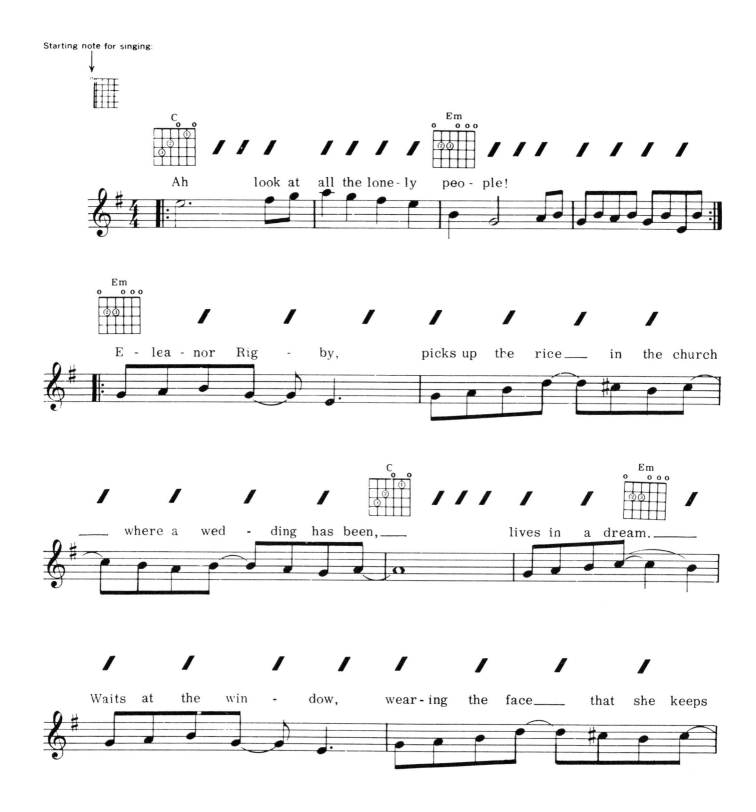

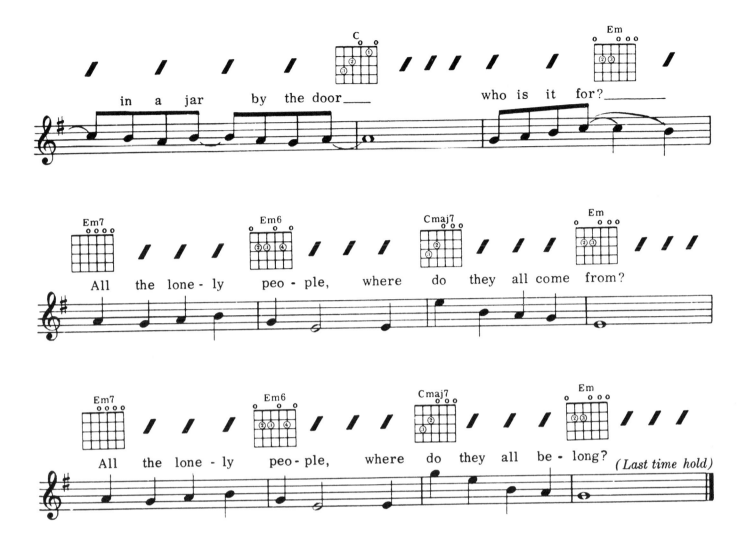

in a jar by the door____ who is it for?_____

All the lone - ly peo - ple, where do they all come from?

All the lone - ly peo - ple, where do they all be - long? *(Last time hold)*

Father McKenzie, writing the words of a sermon that no one will hear, no one comes near.

Look at him working, darning his socks in the night when there's nobody there, what does he care?

All the lonely people, where do they all come from?

All the lonely people, where do they all belong?

Eleanor Rigby, died in the church and was buried along with her name, nobody came.

Father McKenzie, wiping the dirt from his hands as he walks from the grave, no one was saved.

All the lonely people, where do they all come from?

All the lonely people, where do they all belong?

Lying Eyes
Words and music by Glenn Frey and Don Henley

Bright Country style

1. Cit-y girls__ just seem to find__ out ear-ly

how to o - pen doors with just a smile.

A rich old man,__ and she won't have to

wor - ry; she'll dress up all in

lace and go in style.

You can't

hide _____ your ly - in' eyes,

and your smile _____ is a thin ___ dis-

guise. I thought by now _____ you'd re - al -

ize _____ there ain't no way ___ to

To Coda ⊕   *D. C. (with repeats) al Coda* ⊕

hide your ly - in' eyes.

Coda ⊕

eyes.

2. Late at night a big old house gets lonely;
   I guess every form of refuge has its price.
   And it breaks her heart to think her love is only
   Given to a man with hands as cold as ice.

3. So she tells him she must go out for the evening
   To comfort an old friend who's feelin' down.
   But he knows where she's goin' as she's leavin';
   She is headed for the cheatin' side of town.
   (Chorus)

4. She gets up and pours herself a strong one
   And stares out at the stars up in the sky.
   Another night, it's gonna be a long one;
   She draws the shade and hangs her head to cry.

5. My, oh my, you sure know how to arrange things;
   You set it up so well, so carefully.
   Ain't it funny how your new life didn't change things;
   You're still the same old girl you used to be.
   (Chorus)

Killing Me Softly With His Song

Words and music by Charles Fox

— my   eyes.—
— right   on.——
— and   strong.—   Strum-ming my pain— with his fin - gers,—

Sing-ing my life— with his words.—   Kill-ing me soft - ly with his—

— song, Kill-ing me soft - ly——— with his— song.   Tell-ing my whole—

— life   with his—— words, Kill-ing me soft - ly

1.2.

3.

with his   song.—

117

Proud Mary
Words and music by John C. Fogerty

Moderately (with a heavy beat)

Verse:

G

Left a good job___ in the cit-y,___ Work-in' for The Man ev-'ry
Cleaned a lot of plates in___ Mem-phis,_ Pumped a lot of pain in___

night and day,___ And I nev-er lost one min-ute of___ sleep-in',
New Or-leans,_ But I nev-er saw the good_ side of the cit-y, Un-

Wor-ry-in' 'bout the way things__ might have___ been.__)
til I hitched a ride on a riv-er boat queen.__ }

Chorus:

Big wheel keep on turn-in',— Proud Mar-y keep on burn - in',— Roll-

in',— roll - in',— roll - in' on the riv - er.——

Verse:

If you come down to the riv - er, Bet you gon -na find some peo-

- ple who live.— You don't have to wor-ry— 'cause you have no mon - ey,—

Peo - ple on the riv - er are hap - py to give.—

Coda *Repeat and fade*

Roll-in',— roll - in',— roll-in' on the riv - er.——

119

Jailhouse Rock

Words and music by Jerry Lieber and Mike Stoller

Medium bright Rock

1. The war-den threw a party in the coun-ty jail.___ The
2. Spi-der Mur-phy play'd the ten-or sax-o-phone.___
3. Number For-ty-sev-en said to Num-ber Three.___

pri-son band was there and they be-gan to wail.___ The
Lit-tle Joe was blow-in' on the slide trom-bone.___ The
"You're the cut-est jail-bird I ev-er did see.___ I

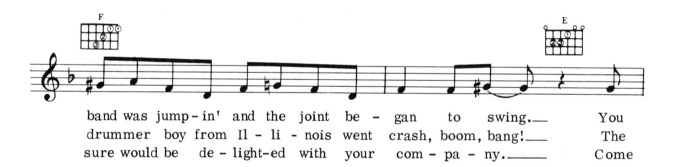

band was jump-in' and the joint be-gan to swing.___ You
drummer boy from Il-li-nois went crash, boom, bang!___ The
sure would be de-light-ed with your com-pa-ny.___ Come

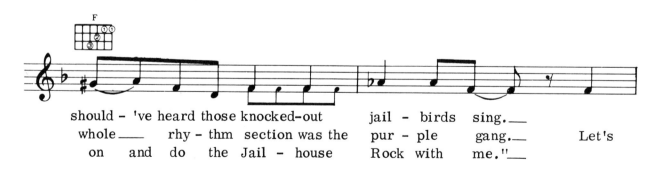

should-'ve heard those knocked-out jail-birds sing.___
whole___ rhy-thm section was the pur-ple gang.___ Let's
on and do the Jail-house Rock with me."___

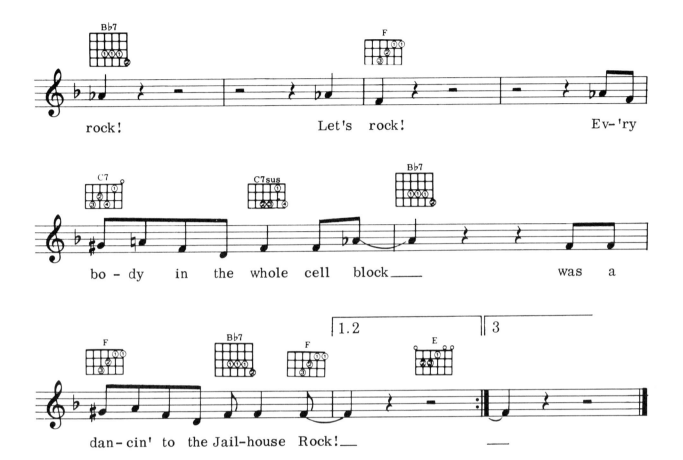

rock!   Let's   rock!   Ev-'ry

bo - dy   in   the   whole   cell   block____   was   a

dan - cin'   to   the   Jail-house   Rock!__   ___

EXTRA CHORUSES

4.   The sad sack was a-sittin' on a block of stone,
Way over in the corner weeping all alone.
The warden said, "Hey buddy, don't you be no square,
If you can't find a partner, use a wooden chair!"
Let's rock, etc.

5.   Shifty Henry said to Bugs, "For Heaven's sake,
No one s lookin', now's our chance to make a break."
Bugsy turned to Shifty and he said, "Nix, nix,
I wanna stick around a while and get my kicks,"
Let's rock, etc.

Little Deuce Coupe

Words and music by Roger Christian and Brian Wilson

com - pe - ti - tion clutch, with four on the floor___ yeah, she

purrs like a kit - ten till the lake pipes roar,___ and if that ain't e - nough to make you

flip your wig, there's one more thing, I've got the pink slip, dad - dy! And

com - in' off the line, when the lights turn green, she blows 'em out of the wa - ter like you've

nev - er seen.___ I get pushed out of shape,___ and it's hard to steer,___ when

I get rub - ber in a all four gears.___ She's my lit - tle deuce coupe,

Repeat and fade

you don't know___ what I've got! _____ She's got a

123

Mr. Bojangles
Words and music by Jerry Jeff Walker

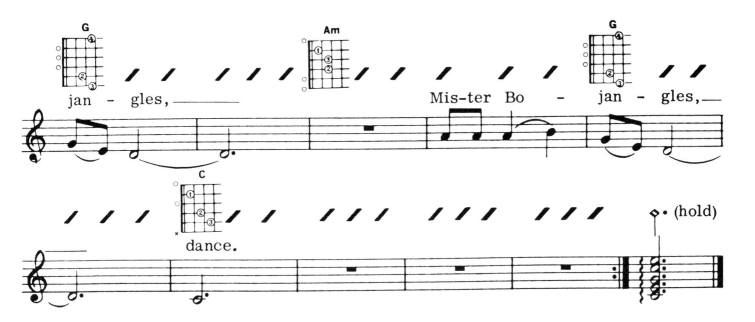

jan - gles, _____ Mis-ter Bo - jan - gles,__

dance. ⌒• (hold)

ADDITIONAL WORDS

2. I met him in a cell in New Orleans
   I was down and out.
   He looked at me to be the eyes of age,
   As he spoke right out.
   He talked of life,
   Talked of life.
   He laughed, slapped his leg a step.
   Mr. Bojangles, (etc.)

3. He said his name, Bojangles,
   Then he danced a lick across the cell.
   He grabbed his pants a better stance,
   Oh, he jumped up high,
   He clicked his heels.
   He let go a laugh,
   Let go a laugh,
   Shook back his clothes all around.
   Mr. Bojangles, (etc.)

4. He danced for those at minstrel shows
   And county fairs throughout the South.
   He spoke with tears of fifteen years
   How his dog and he traveled about.
   His dog up and died,
   He up and died,
   After twenty years he still grieved.
   Mr. Bojangles, (etc.)

5. He said, "I dance now at ev'ry chance
   In honky tonks for drinks and tips.
   But most of the time I spend
   Behind these county bars,"
   He said, "I drinks a bit."
   He shook his head and as he shook his head,
   I heard someone ask please,
   Mr. Bojangles, (etc.)

After The Goldrush

Words and music by Neil Young

1. Well, I dreamed I saw the knights in ar-mor com-in', say-in' some-thing a-bout _____ a queen. There were peas-ants sing-in' and drum-mers drum-min' and the arch-er split the tree. There was a fan-fare blow-in' to the sun _ that was float-ing on the breeze.

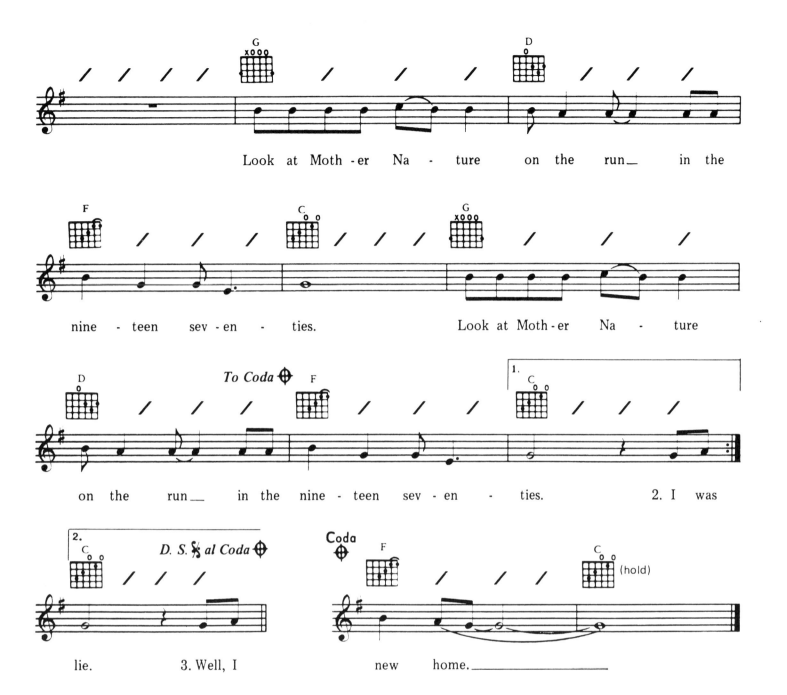

Look at Moth-er Na - ture on the run_ in the
nine - teen sev - en - ties. Look at Moth -er Na - ture
on the run__ in the nine - teen sev - en - ties. 2. I was
lie. 3. Well, I new home.___

2. I was lyin' in a burned-out basement with the full moon in my eyes.
I was hopin' for replacement when the sun burst through the sky.
There was a band playin' in my head and I felt like getting high.
I was thinkin' about what a friend had said, I was hopin' it was a lie.
Thinkin' about what a friend had said, I was hopin' it was a lie.

3. Well, I dreamed I saw the silver spaceships flyin' in the yellow haze of the sun.
There were children cryin' and colors flyin' all around the chosen ones.
All in a dream, all in a dream, the loading had begun.
Flying Mother Nature's silver seed to a new home in the sun.
Flying Mother Nature's silver seed to a new home.

Mellow Yellow

Words and music by Donovan Leitch

129

Angel
Words and music by Jimi Hendrix

Slowly, with a beat

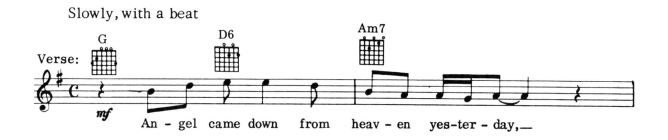

Verse: An - gel came down from heav - en yes-ter - day,—

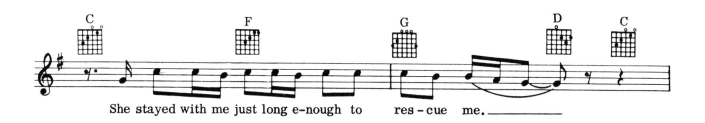

She stayed with me just long e-nough to res - cue me.——

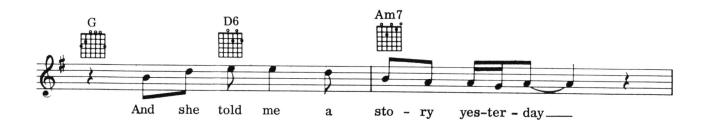

And she told me a sto - ry yes-ter - day——

a–bout the sweet love be-tween the moon and the deep blue sea.———

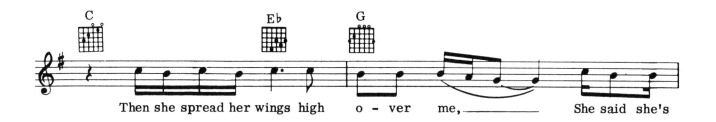

Then she spread her wings high o - ver me, _____ She said she's

gon - na come back to - mor - row. And I said:

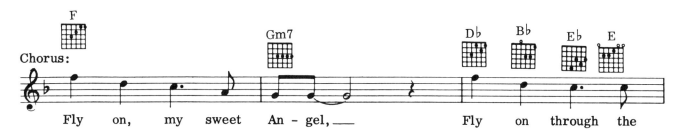

Chorus:

Fly on, my sweet An - gel, ___ Fly on through the

sky. _____ Fly on, my sweet An - gel, ___ To -

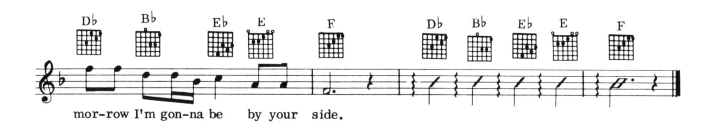

mor-row I'm gon-na be by your side.

Verse 2. Sure enough, this woman came home to me
        Silver wings silhouetted against a child's sunrise
        And my Angel, she said unto me
        Today is the day for you to rise.

        Take my hand
        You're gonna be my man
        You're gonna rise
        Then she took me high over yonder.

        And I said: (Chorus)

After Midnight
Words and music by John J. Cale

Lady D'Arbanville

Words and music by Cat Stevens

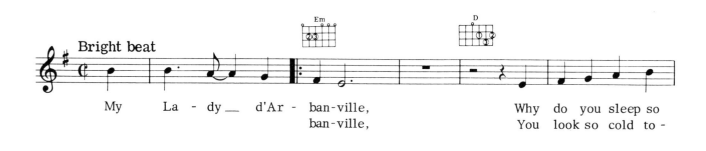

My La - dy ___ d'Ar - ban-ville,   Why do you sleep so
ban - ville,   You look so cold to -

still?   I'll wake you ___ to - mor-row,   And
night,   Your lips feel ___ like win - ter;   Your

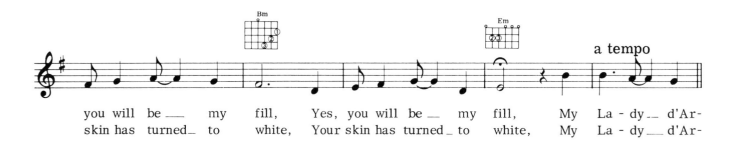

a tempo

you will be ___ my fill, Yes, you will be ___ my fill, My La - dy ___ d'Ar-
skin has turned ___ to white, Your skin has turned ___ to white, My La - dy ___ d'Ar-

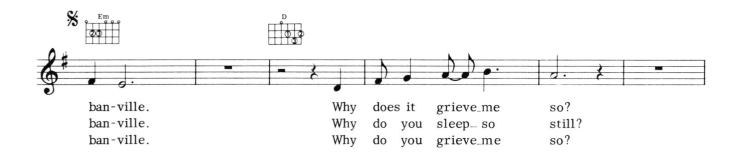

ban - ville.   Why does it grieve ___ me so?
ban - ville.   Why do you sleep ___ so still?
ban - ville.   Why do you grieve ___ me so?

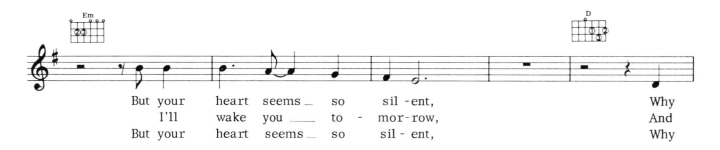

But your heart seems ___ so sil - ent,   Why
I'll wake you ___ to - mor - row,   And
But your heart seems ___ so sil - ent,   Why

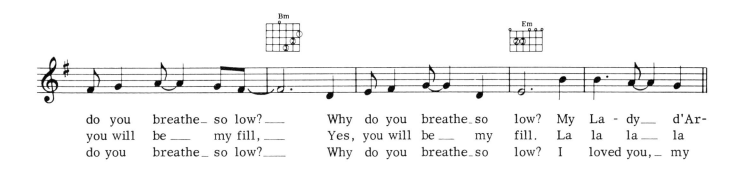

do you   breathe_ so low?___   Why   do   you   breathe_so   low? My   La - dy__   d'Ar-
you will   be __ my fill, ___   Yes, you will be __ my   fill. La   la   la __   la
do you   breathe_ so low?___   Why   do   you   breathe_so   low? I   loved you, _   my

ban-ville,   Why   do   you   sleep_so   still?
la   la.   La   la   la   la __ la   la.
la - dy,   Though   in   your   grave_you   lie,

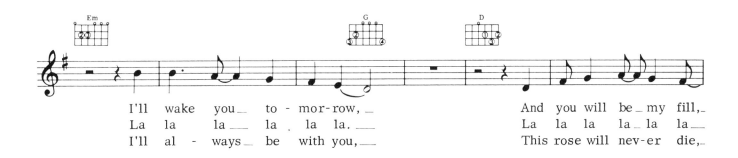

I'll   wake   you_   to - mor-row, _   And   you will   be _ my   fill,_
La   la   la __   la .   la   la. ___   La   la   la   la _ la   la__
I'll   al - ways_   be   with   you,__   This   rose will   nev-er   die,_

1

___   Yes,   you will   be _ my   fill.   My   La - dy_   d'Ar-
___   la   la   la   la _   la
___   This   rose will   nev - er

2

freely

la.   My

D.%. al ⊕   *Coda*

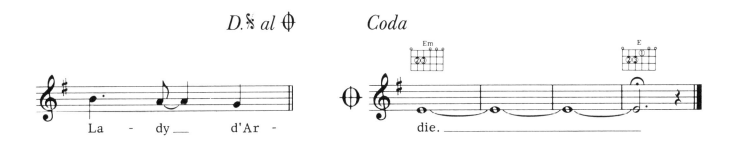

La - dy_   d'Ar -   die._____

And I Love Her

Words and music by John Lennon and Paul McCartney

Desperado

Words and music by Glenn Frey and Don Henley

Slowly

Des - per - a - do, why don't you come to your sens - es? You been
a - do, oh, you ain't get - tin' no young - er, your

out rid - in' fenc - es for so long now. ___ Oh, you're a
pain and your hun - ger, they're driv - in' you home. And

hard one, I know that you got your rea - sons, these
free - dom, well, that's just some peo - ple talk - in', your

things that are pleas - in' you can hurt you some-how. Don't you
pris - on is walk - in' through this world all a - lone. Don't your

draw the queen of dia - monds, boy, she'll beat you if she's a - ble, you know the
feet get cold in the win' - ter time? The sky won't snow and the sun won't shine, it's

queen of hearts is al - ways your best bet. Now it
hard to tell the night - time from the day. You're

138

seems to   me   some fine things have been   laid   up - on your   ta - ble,   but you
los - in'   all   your highs and lows. Ain't it fun - ny   how the feel - in' goes a -

on - ly want the ones that you can't   get.   Des - per -   way? _____

_____   Des - per - a - do,   why don't you   come to your sens - es?   Come

down from your fenc - es,   o - pen   the gate.   It   may   be

rain - in',   but there's a   rain - bow a - bove ___ you. You bet - ter

let some - bod - y love you   you bet - ter

let some - bod - y love you   be - fore   it's   too _____   late.

139

Got A Lot Of Livin' To Do
Words and music by Aaron Schroeder and Ben Weisman

Bright tempo

VERSE

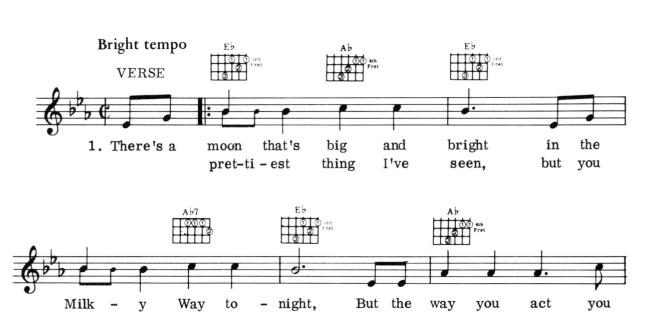

1. There's a moon that's big and bright in the
pret-ti-est thing I've seen, but you

Milk-y Way to-night, But the way you act you
treat me so dog-gone mean, Ain't-cha got no heart? I'm

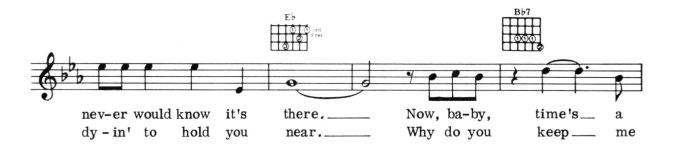

nev-er would know it's there.____ Now, ba-by, time's__ a
dy-in' to hold you near.____ Why do you keep___ me

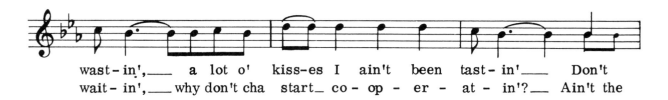

wast-in',___ a lot o' kiss-es I ain't been tast-in'___ Don't
wait-in',___ why don't cha start__ co-op-er-at-in'?___ Ain't the

know a-bout you but I'm a gon-na get my share.___
things_ I say the things_ you_ wan-na hear?___

CHORUS

I Say A Little Prayer

Words and music by Hal David and Burt Bacharach

Moderately fast, smooth

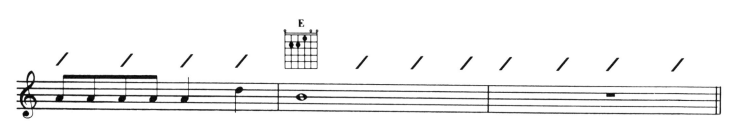

1. The mo - ment I wake up, _____ be - fore _ I put
2. I run _ for the bus dear, _____ while rid - ing I

on my make - up, _____ I say a lit - tle prayer for you. __
think of us dear. _____ I say a lit - tle prayer for you. __

While comb - ing my hair now _____ and won - d'ring what
At work _ I just take time _____ and all _ through my

dress to wear now, _____ I say a lit-tle prayer for you. __ For-
cof-fee break time _____ I say a lit-tle prayer for you. __

ev-er, for-ev-er you'll stay in my heart__ and I will love you__ for-

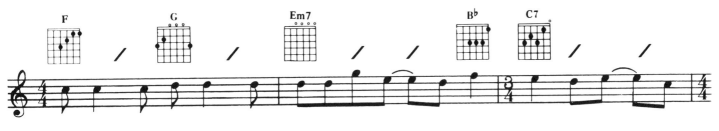

ev-er and ev-er. We nev-er will part.__ Oh, how I'll love you.__ To-

geth-er, to-geth-er, that's how it must be.__ To live with-out you__ would

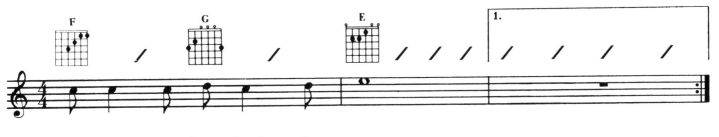

on-ly mean heart-break for me.

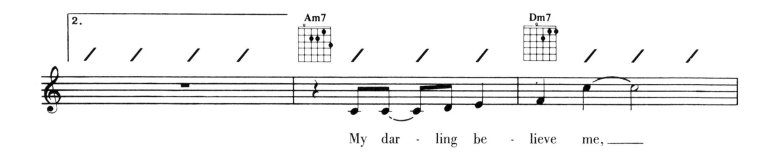

My dar - ling be - lieve me, _____

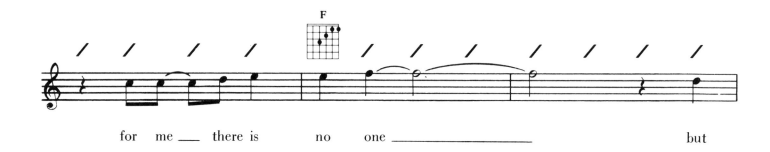

for me __ there is   no   one _____   but

you.   Please_love me   too.   I'm __ in love with

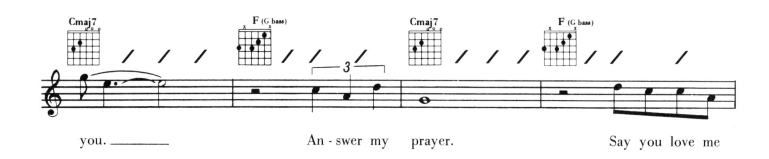

you. _____   An - swer my   prayer.   Say you love me

too. _____

Day Tripper

Words and music by John Lennon and Paul McCartney

2. She's a big teaser, She took me half the way there.
   She's a big teaser, She took me half the way there now.
   She was a Day Tripper, One way ticket, Yeh!
   It took me so long to find out, and I found out.

3. Tried to please her, She only played one night stands.
   Tried to please her, She only played one night stands.
   She was a Day Tripper, Sunday driver, Yeh!
   It took me so long to find out, and I found out.

You Don't Mess Around With Jim
Words and music by Jim Croce

CHORUS

And they say,__ "You don't tug on Su-per-man's cape, You don't

spit in-to the wind,__ You don't pull the mask off the

old Lone Rang-er and you don't mess a-round with Jim."__

To Coda

Well out-a south Al-a-bam-a come a

coun-try boy. He said,"I'm look-in' for a man named Jim,__ I am a

pool shoot-in' boy, my name is Wil-lie Mc-Coy__ but down home they call me Slim.__

__ Yeah, I'm look-in' for the king of For-ty-Sec-ond Street, He driv-in' a drop-

147

Hey Joe

Words and music by William M. Roberts

Bright rock beat

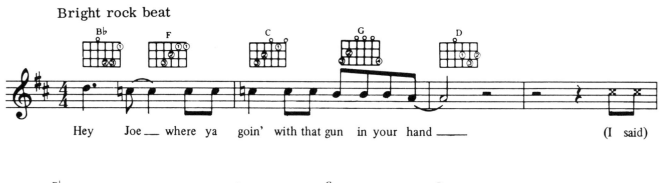

Hey Joe ___ where ya goin' with that gun in your hand ___ (I said)

Hey Joe ___ where ya goin' with that gun in your hand ___ I'm go-in'

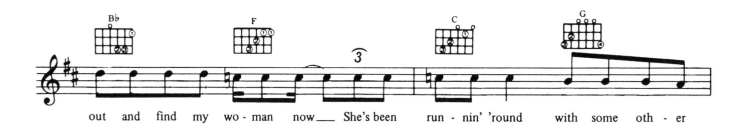

out and find my wo-man now ___ She's been run-nin' 'round with some oth-er

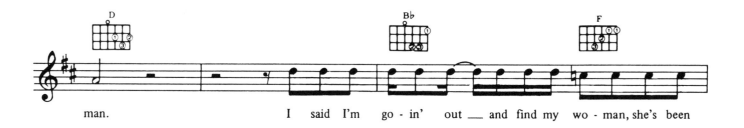

man. I said I'm go-in' out ___ and find my wo-man, she's been

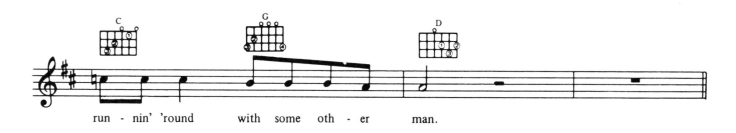

run-nin' 'round with some oth-er man.

1. Hey Joe ____ tell me what are ____ you gon-na do ____
2. Hey Joe ____ tell me where are ____ you gon-na go ____

Hey Joe ____ tell me what are ____ you gon-na do ____ Well, I
Hey Joe ____ tell me where are ____ you gon-na go ____ Well, I

guess I'll ____ shoot my ____ wo-man, that's what I'll do ____
think I'll go down to my fav-'rite place, Mex-i-co ____

Well, I guess I'll ____ shoot 'em both be-fore ____ I'm
Well, I think I'll go down to where a man ____ can be

through.   And   there ain't gon-na be no hang-man's
free.

ropes gon-na be put a-round me. ____

151

Monday Monday

Words and music by John Phillips

eve - nin' you would still be here___ with me.
Mon -day how could you leave and not___ take

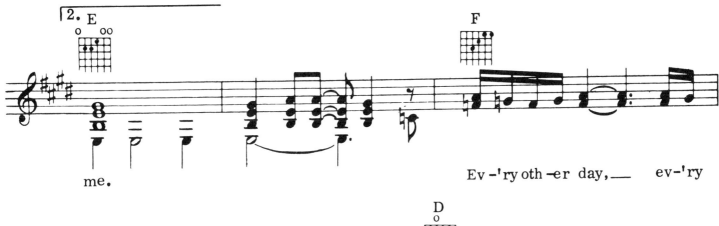

me.   Ev -'ry oth -er day,___ ev -'ry

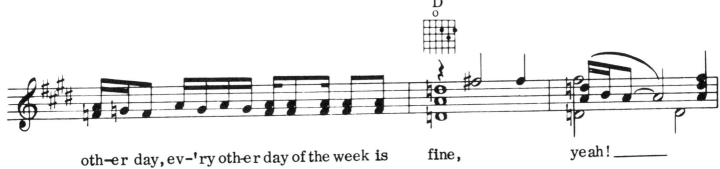

oth-er day, ev-'ry oth-er day of the week is   fine,   yeah! _____

But when-ev-er Mon -day comes,   but when-ev-er Mon-day comes you can find me

D.C. and fade

cry'n',   yeah! _____

153

Lowdown
Words and music by David Paich and Boz Scaggs

Moderately, with a beat

1. Ba - by's in - to run-nin' 'round, hang - in' with the crowd,

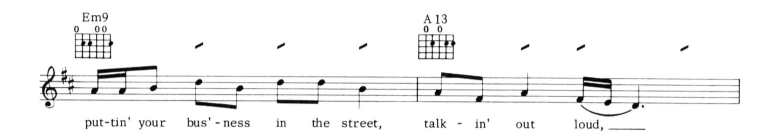

put-tin' your bus' - ness in the street, talk - in' out loud, ____

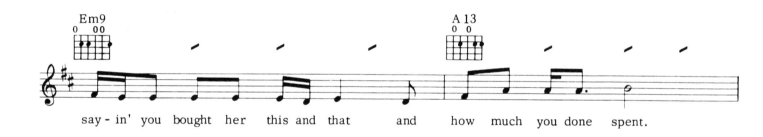

say - in' you bought her this and that and how much you done spent.

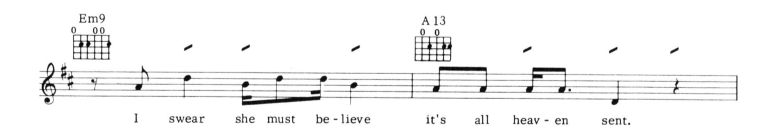

I swear she must be - lieve it's all heav - en sent.

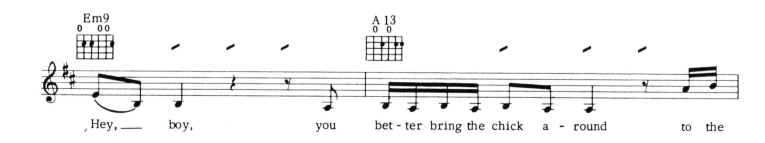

, Hey, ____ boy, you bet - ter bring the chick a - round to the

154

sad, sad truth, the dirt-y low-down.___ Who,_____

___ I won - der, won - der, won - der, won - der

who___ taught her how to talk like that. I

won- der, won- der, won- der, won-der who.___ who.___

2. Nothin' you can't handle, nothin' you ain't got.
   Put your money on the table; drive it off the lot.
   Turn on that old love light and turn a "maybe" to a "yes."
   Same old school boy game got you into this mess.
   Hey, son, you better get on back to town.
   Face the sad old truth, the dirty lowdown.
   Who, I wonder, wonder, wonder, wonder who
   Put those ideas in your head.
   I wonder, wonder, wonder, wonder who.

3. You ain't got to be so bad, got to be so cold.
   This dog-eat-dog existence sure is gettin' old.
   Gotta have a jones for this, jones for that.
   This runnin' with the Joneses, boy, just ain't where it's at.
   Ah, ha, you gonna come back around
   To the sad, sad truth, the dirty lowdown.
   Who, I wonder, wonder, wonder, wonder who
   Got you thinkin' like that, boy.
   I wonder, wonder, wonder, wonder who.

(I Can't Get No) Satisfaction

Words and music by Mick Jagger and Keith Richard

With a beat

CHORUS

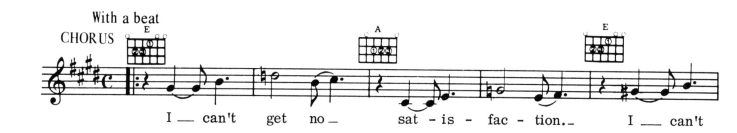

I __ can't get no __ sat - is - fac - tion. __ I __ can't

get no __ sat - is - fac - tion, 'Cause I try, and I

Last time (girl with ac - tion,)

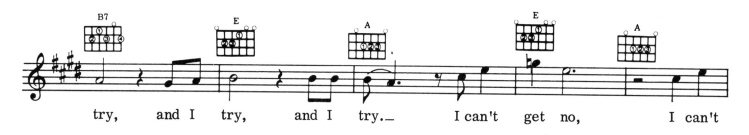

try, and I try, and I try. __ I can't get no, I can't

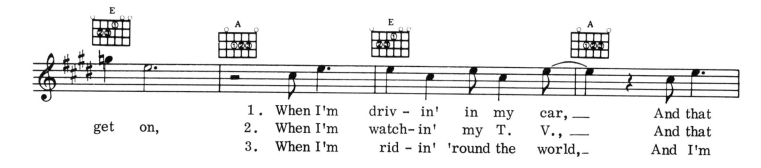

get on,
1. When I'm driv - in' in my car, __ And that
2. When I'm watch - in' my T. V., __ And that
3. When I'm rid - in' 'round the world, __ And I'm

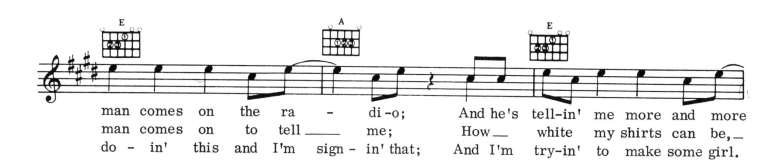

man comes on the ra - di - o; And he's tell-in' me more and more
man comes on to tell ____ me; How __ white my shirts can be, __
do - in' this and I'm sign - in' that; And I'm try-in' to make some girl.

a - bout some use - less in - for - ma - tion, Supposed to
Well, he can't be a man, 'cause he ___ does - n't smoke the
Who tells me ba - by, bet-ter come back let - er next week, 'cos you

fire my im-ag - i - na - tion. I can't
same cig--a-rettes as me. ___ I can't get no Oh, no, no, no,
see I'm on a los - ing streak. I can't

Hey, hey, hey. ___ that's what I say. ___

I can't get no, I can't get no, I can't

get no Sat-is - fac - tion, no sat-is - fac - tion,

no sat-is - fac -tion, no sat-is - fac-tion.

Southern Man

Words and music by Neil Young

I ___ saw cot - ton ___ and I ___ saw
Lil - lie Bell your hair is gold - en

black, tall ___ white man - sions ___ and
brown, I've ___ seen your black ___ man

lit - tle shacks; south-ern
com - in' 'round; swear by

man, when will you pay ___ them back? I ___ heard
God, I'm gon - na cut ___ him down!

scream - in' ___ and bull ___ whips crack - in'. ___

How ___ long, how long? ___ Ah! _____

Repeat and fade

159

Here, There and Everywhere

Words and music by John Lennon and Paul McCartney

Moderately slow

Here,
There,
mak-ing each day of the year,
run-ning my hands thru her hair,

chang-ing my life with a wave of her hand;
both of us think - ing how good it can be;

No - bod - y can de - ny that there's some -thing there.
Some - one is speak - ing but she does -n't know he's

1.

2.

there. I want her ev - 'ry - where and if

she's be - side me I know I need nev - er care.

But to love her is to meet her ev -'ry-where, know-ing that love is to

share, each one be - lieve -ing that love nev - er dies,

Watch-ing her eyes and hop - ing I'm al - ways there. To be there and

ev - 'ry - where, here there and ev - 'ry-where, _____ (hold)

I Get Around
Words and music by Brian Wilson

Medium Rock beat

I get a - round _____ from town to town _____ I'm a real cool head _____

I'm mak - in' real good bread. _____

1. I'm get - tin' bugged, driv - in' up an' down the same ol' strip _____ I got - ta
(2. We) al - ways take my car 'cause it's nev - er been beat _____ and we've

find a new place where the kids are hip _____
nev - er missed yet with the girls we meet _____

Guitar Solo _____

My
None of the

bud - dies   and   me ___   are   get - tin'   real   well   known, ___   Yeah,   the
guys   go   stead - y 'cause it   would - n't be right ___   to   leave   your

bad   guys   know   us   and   they   leave   us   a - lone. ___
best   girl   home   on   a   Sat - ur - day   night. ___

Chorus

I   get   a - round _____   from   town   to

town   I'm   a   real   cool   head _____

I'm   mak - in'   real   good   bread. _____   2. We

Repeat and fade

Spoken: I   get   around,

Baby I Love Your Way

Words and music by Peter Frampton

1. Sha - dows grow___ so long___ be - fore my eyes

and they're mov - ing ___ a - cross the page.___

Sud - den - ly___ the day___ turns in - to

night ___ far a - way

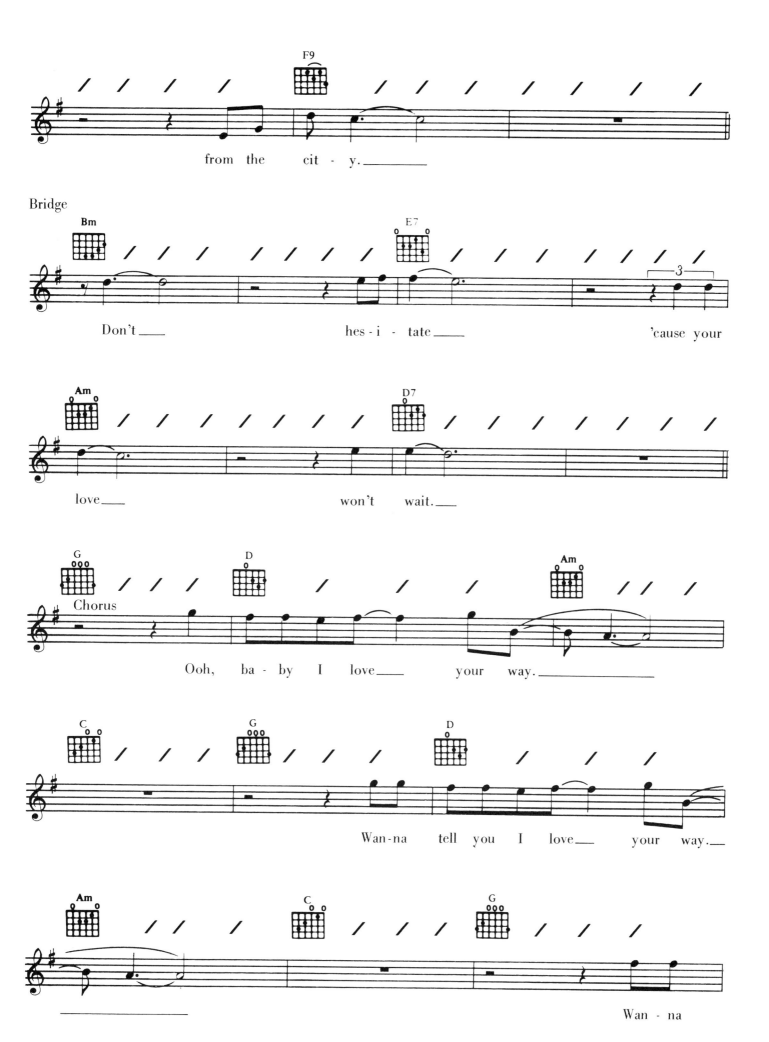

from the cit - y._____

Bridge

Don't _____ hes - i - tate _____ 'cause your

love_____ won't wait._____

Chorus

Ooh, ba - by I love____ your way._____

Wan - na tell you I love____ your way.__

_____ Wan - na

be with you night— and day.——

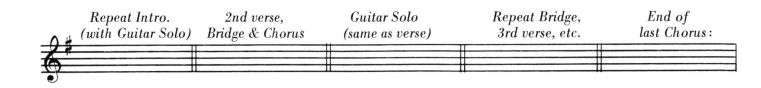

Repeat Intro.   *2nd verse,*   *Guitar Solo*   *Repeat Bridge,*   *End of*
(with Guitar Solo)   *Bridge & Chorus*   *(same as verse)*   *3rd verse, etc.*   *last Chorus:*

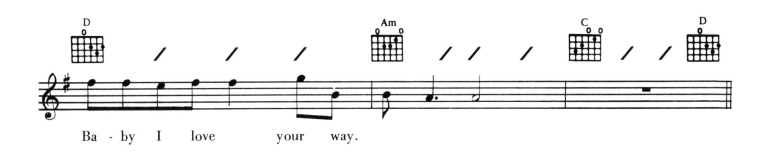

Ba - by   I   love   your   way.

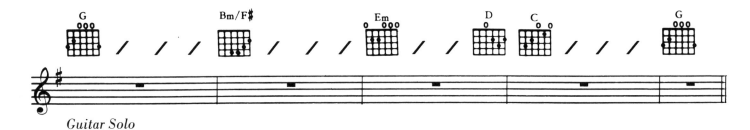

Guitar Solo

2. Moon appears to shine and light the sky with the help of some firefly
   Wonder how they have the power to shine
   I can see them under the pine,
   Don't hesitate 'cause your love won't wait.
   Ooh baby I love your way, wanna tell you I love your way
   Wanna be with you night and day.
   (Guitar Solo)
   Don't hesitate, 'cause your love won't wait.

3. I can see the sunset in your eyes, brown and grey and blue besides
   Clouds are stalking islands in the sun.
   I wish I could buy one out of season.
   Don't hesitate 'cause your love won't wait.
   Ooh baby I love your way, wanna tell you I love your way
   Wanna be with you night and day, ooh baby I love your way.

If Six Was Nine

Words and music by Jimi Hendrix

With a moving beat

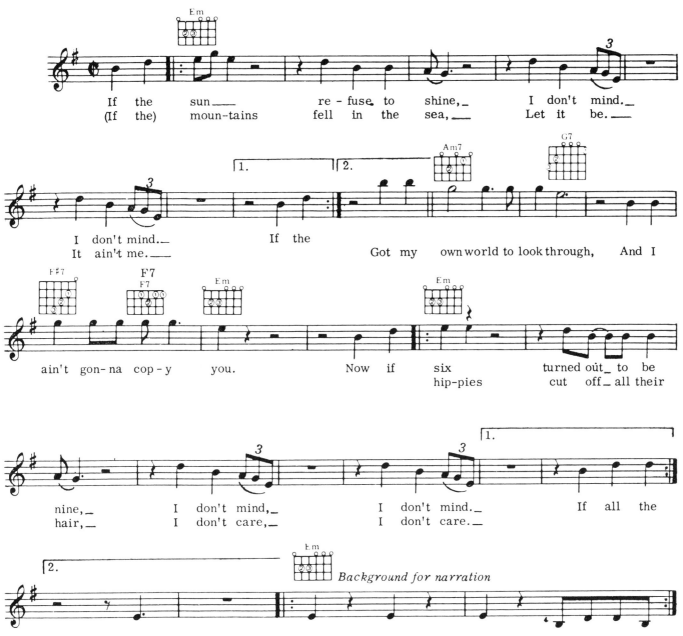

If the sun___ re-fuse to shine,_ I don't mind._
(If the) moun-tains fell in the sea, ___ Let it be. ___

I don't mind._
It ain't me.___ If the

Got my own world to look through, And I

ain't gon-na cop-y you. Now if six
hip-pies turned out_ to be
cut off_ all their

nine,_ I don't mind,_ I don't mind._ If all the
hair,_ I don't care,_ I don't care._

Background for narration

Dig!

Spoken: White collared conservative flashing down the street, pointing their plastic finger at me. They're hoping soon my kind will drop and die, but I'm gonna wave my freak flag high, high. I'm the one who has to die when it's time for me to die, so let me live my life the way I want to! Sing on, brother, play on, drummer! (Music fade out)

Tupelo Honey
Words and music by Van Morrison

1. You can take all the tea in Chi - na,

put it in a big brown bag for me;

sail right round all the sev - en o - ceans,

drop it straight in - to __ the deep blue sea.

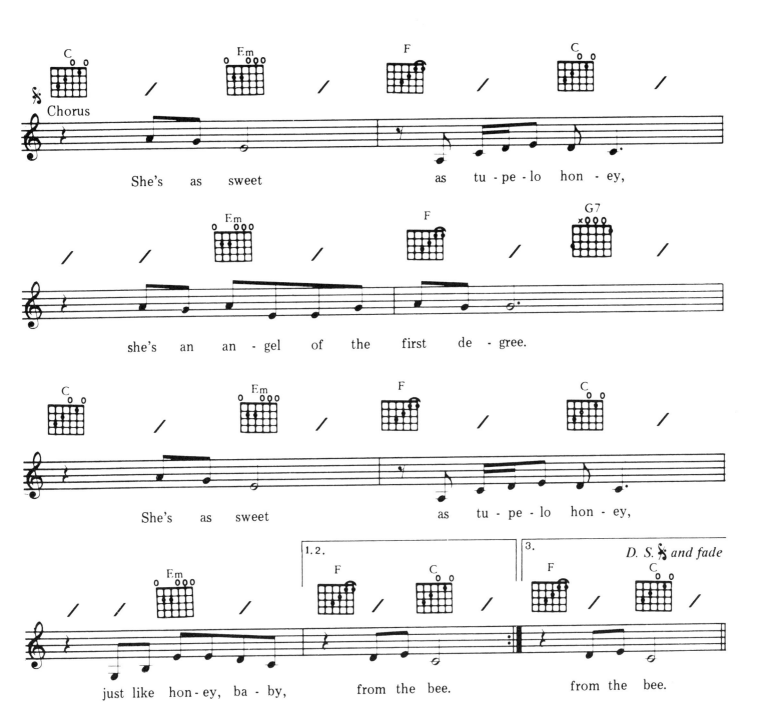

2. You can't stop us on the road to freedom;
   You can't keep us 'cause our eyes can see.
   Men with insight, men in granite,
   Knights in armour bent on chivalry.
   (Chorus)

3. I'll tell a tale of old Manhattan,
   Adirondack bus to go.
   Standing waiting on my number,
   And my number's gonna show.
   (Chorus)

Return To Sender

Words and music by Otis Blackwell and Winfield Scott

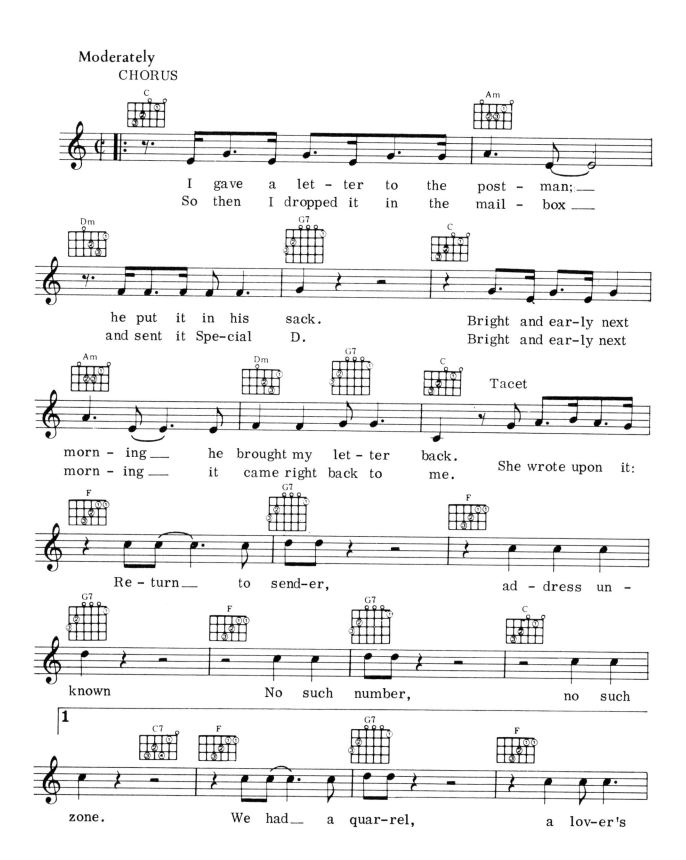

spat.   I   write I'm sor - ry but my

let – ter keeps coming back.   zone.   This time I'm gonna

take it my – self   and put it right in her   hand.   And

if it comes back the ver – y next day,   Then I'll un – der – stand

___   the writ-ing on it.   Re- turn___   to send-er,

ad – dress un – known.   No such number,

no such zone.   zone.___

Change Partners

Words and music by Stephen Stills

Slowly, in 2

Verse

1. All of the la-dies at-tend-ing the ball are re-quest-ed to gaze in the

fac-es found on their dance card.

Please then re-mem-ber and don't get too close___ to one spe-cial one, he will

take your de-fens-es and run. _____ Chorus So we

Moderate Rock beat

change _____ part-ners, time to change _____

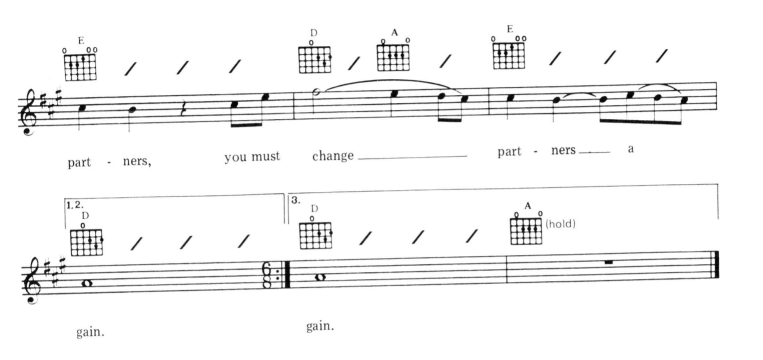

part - ners,   you must   change _____ part - ners___ a

gain.   gain.

2. This is how most of our ladies grew up;
   At the country club dances they learned how to handle the boys.
   Gently but firmly they learned to say no;
   There were four more young men who were waiting in the color and the noise.
                 (Chorus)

3. All of the ladies attending the ball
   Are requested to gaze in the faces found on their dance card.
   Please then remember and follow your list
   'Cause the dear things get hurt and the broken hearts make you feel hard.
                 (Chorus)

Everybody's Talkin'

Words and music by Fred Neil

thru the pour-in'__ rain   Go-in' where the

weath-er__ suits my clothes _____ Bank-in' off of the

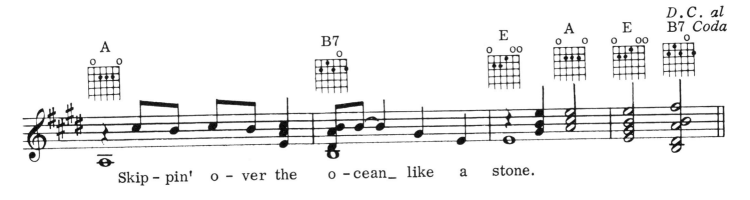

north-east__ wind Sail-in' on a sum-mer__ breeze

D.C. al
Coda

Skip-pin' o-ver the o-cean_ like a stone.

Coda

Repeat and fade

And I won't_ let you leave my love_ be-hind_____ No,

A Hard Day's Night

Words and music by John Lennon and Paul McCartney

D.C. al ⊕ Coda
(use 1st verse)

177

Suzanne
Words and music by Leonard Cohen

1. Su - zanne   takes   you   down _____   to her
2. (And) Je - sus   was   a   sail - or   when He
3. (Su - zanne   takes   you   down _____   to her

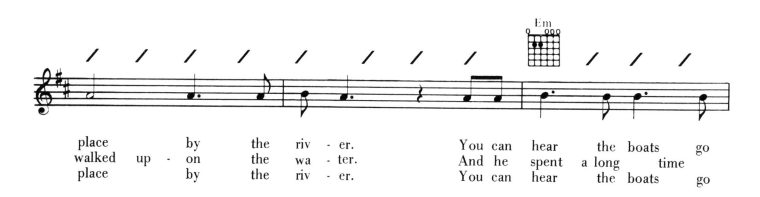

place   by   the   riv - er.   You can   hear   the boats   go
walked   up - on   the   wa - ter.   And he   spent   a long   time
place   by   the   riv - er.   You can   hear   the boats   go

by. __   You   can   spend   the   night   for - ev - er, _____   And you
watch-ing   from   a   lone - ly   wood - en   tow - er, _____   And
by, __   You   can   spend   the   night   for - ev - er, _____   And the

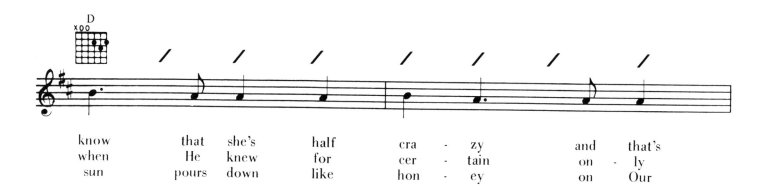

know   that   she's   half   cra - zy   and   that's
when   He   knew   for   cer - tain   on - ly
sun   pours   down   like   hon - ey   on   Our

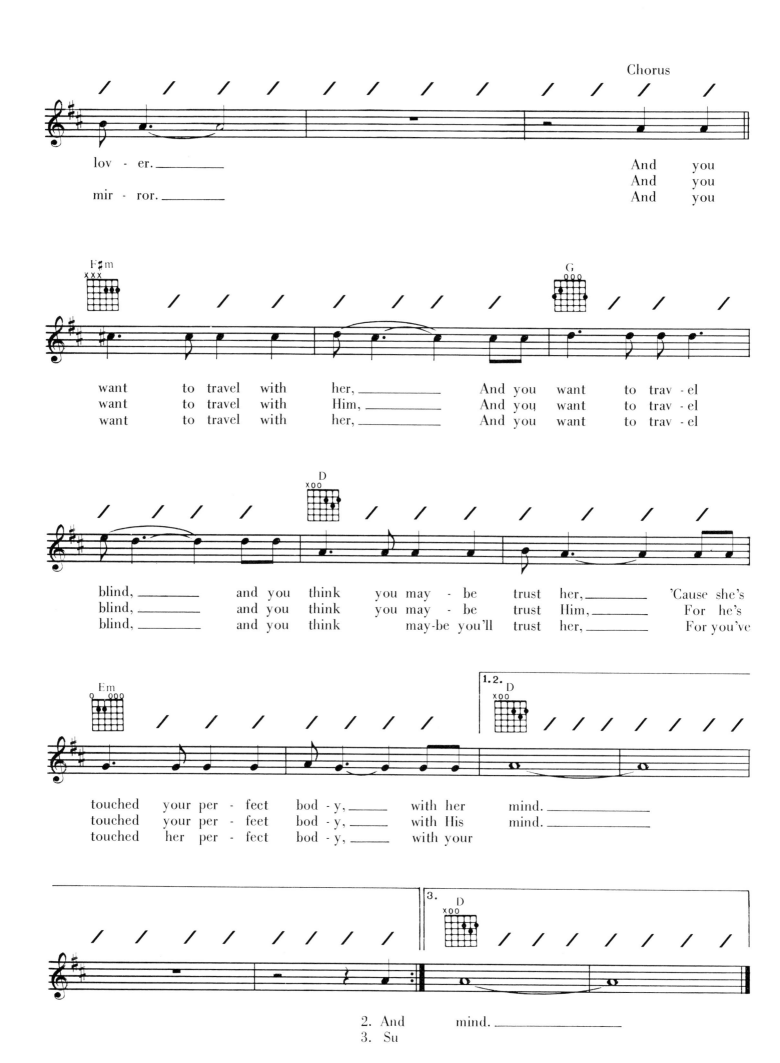

Chorus

lov - er. _____   And   you
                                                           And   you
mir - ror. _____   And   you

F#m   G
want   to travel   with   her, _____   And you want   to trav - el
want   to travel   with   Him, _____   And you want   to trav - el
want   to travel   with   her, _____   And you want   to trav - el

D
blind, _____   and you think   you may - be trust her, _____ 'Cause she's
blind, _____   and you think   you may - be trust Him, _____ For he's
blind, _____   and you think   may-be you'll trust her, _____ For you've

Em   1.2. D
touched your per - fect bod - y, _____ with her   mind. _____
touched your per - fect bod - y, _____ with His   mind. _____
touched her per - fect bod - y, _____ with your

                                            3. D
                                            2. And   mind. _____
                                            3. Su

180

Roots Roots Reggae

Words and music by Vincent Ford

Lively Reggae Feel (accent on 2 and 4)

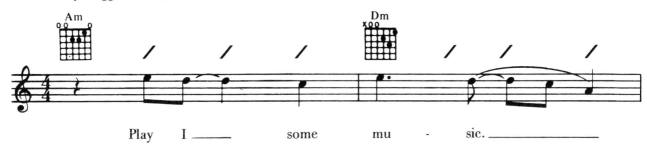

Play I _____ some mu - sic. _____

This is reg - gae mu - sic.   Play I _____ some

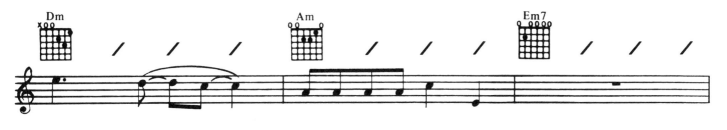

mu - sic. _____ This a reg - gae mu - sic.

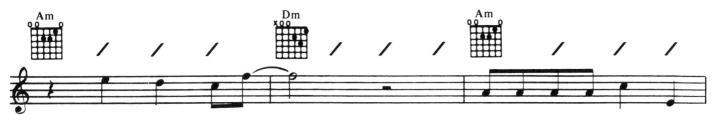

Roots, rocks, reg - gae. _____   This is reg - gae mu - sic.

Roots, rock, reg - gae. _____

This a reg - gae mu - sic.   Hey   mis - ter mu -

sic,___   sure   sound   good   to   me.___

I   can't   re - fuse___   it, ___   what to be   got   to be.___

___   Feel   like   danc - in', ___

dance   'cause   we   are   free.___   Feel   like   danc -

in', ___   come   dance   with   me.___

Down On The Corner

Words and music by John C. Fogerty

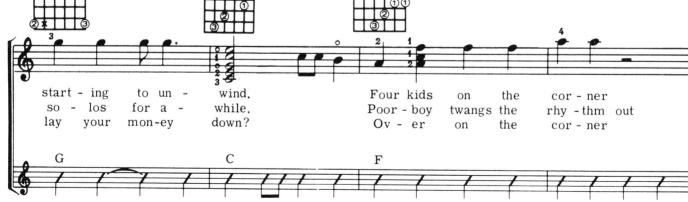

try-ing to   bring   you   up.   Wil - ly   picks   a
on   his   kala - ma -   zoo.   Wil - ly   goes   in -
there's   a   hap - py   noise.   Peo - ple   come   from

tune   out   and   he   blows   it   on   the   harp.
to   a   dance   and   dou - bles   on   ka -   zoo.   Down   on   the
all   a - round   to   watch   the   mag - ic   boy.

cor - ner,   out   in   the   street,   Wil - ly   and   the   Poor boys   are

play - in!   Bring   a   nick - el;   tap   your   feet.   feet.

Country Comfort

Words and music by Elton John and Bernie Taupin

Slowly

1. Soon the pines will be fall - ing ev - 'ry - where;

vil - lage chil - dren fight each oth - er for a

share. And the Six - O - Nine goes

roar - ing past the creek; Dea - con

Lee pre - pares his ser - mon for next week. 2. I saw

grand-ma yes - ter - day down at the store;

well, she's real-ly go-ing fine___ for eight-y -

four.   Well, she   asked me   if   some -

time___ I'd   fix her barn;_____   poor old

girl, she needs   a   hand___ to run the farm._____   And it's

good old   coun-try   com-fort   in   my   bones,_____

just the   sweet-est   sound   my   ears   have ev - er

187

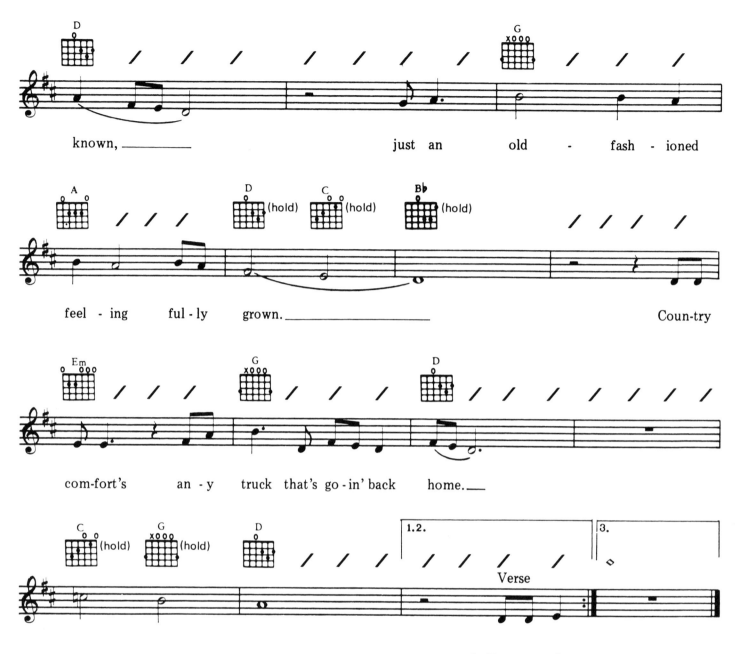

known, _____ just an old - fash - ioned

feel - ing ful - ly grown._____ Coun-try

com-fort's an - y truck that's go - in' back home.__

Verse

3. Down at the

3. Down at the well they've got a new machine;
   Foreman says it cuts manpower by fifteen.
   But that ain't natural, so old Clay would say;
   He's a horse-drawn man until his dying day.
   (Chorus)

4. Now the old fat goose is flying 'cross the sticks;
   The hedgehog's done in clay between the bricks.
   And the rocking chair's a-creaking on the porch;
   Across the valley moves the herdsman with his torch.
   (Chorus)

Strawberry Fields Forever

Words and music by John Lennon and Paul McCartney

Let me take you down 'cause I'm goin' to
   Strawberry Fields.
Nothing is real, and nothing to get hung about,
Strawberry fields forever.
No one I think is in my tree,
I mean it must be high or low.
That is you know you can't tune in but
   it's all right.
That is, I think it's not too bad.

Let me take you down 'cause I'm goin' to
   Strawberry Fields.
Nothing is real, and nothing to get hung about,
Strawberry fields forever.
Always know, sometimes think it's me.
But you know and I know it's a dream.
I think I know of thee, ah yes but it's all
   wrong.
That is, I think I disagree.

189

Season Of The Witch

Words and music by Donovan Leitch

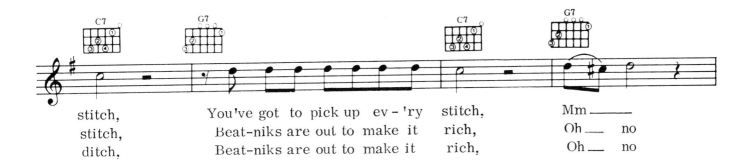

stitch,   You've got to pick up ev - 'ry stitch.   Mm _____

stitch,   Beat-niks are out to make it rich,   Oh __ no

ditch,   Beat-niks are out to make it rich,   Oh __ no

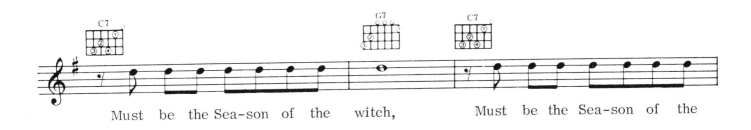

Must be the Sea-son of the witch,   Must be the Sea-son of the

to Coda ⊕

witch,   Yeah,—   Must be the Sea - son of the witch.

D.S. al Coda ⊕ CODA

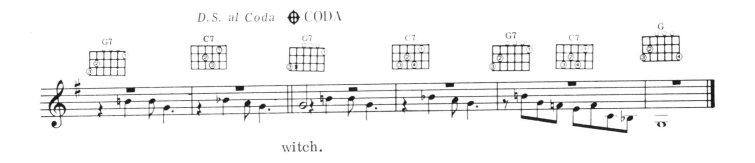

witch.

191

Rainy Day People

Words and music by Gordon Lightfoot

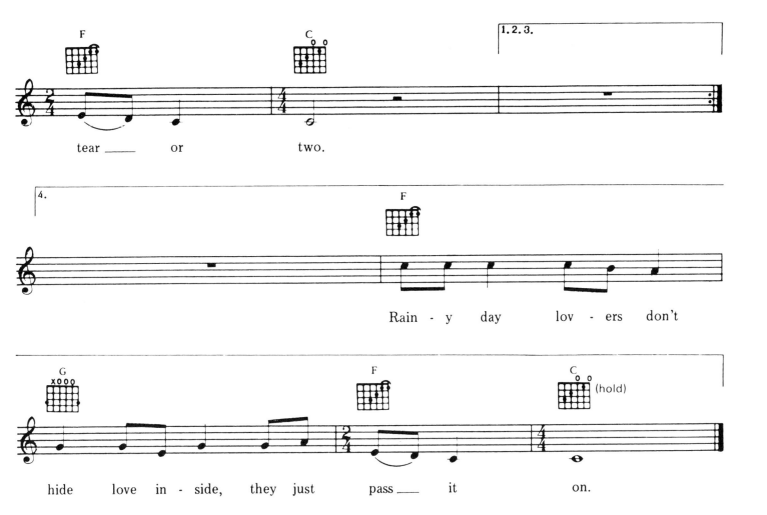

tear ____ or two.

Rain - y day lov - ers don't

hide love in - side, they just pass ____ it on.

2. If you get lonely all you really need is that rainy day love;
   Rainy day people all know there's no sorrow they can't rise above.
   Rainy day lovers don't love any others, that would not be kind;
   Rainy day people all know how it hangs on your peace of mind.

3. *Instrumental* ————————————————

   Rainy day lovers don't lie when they tell ya they bin down there too;
   Rainy day people don't mind if you're cryin' a tear or two.

4. Rainy day people always seem to know when you're feelin' blue;
   High-steppin' strutters who land in the gutter sometimes need one too.
   Take it or leave it or try to believe it if you bin down too long;
   Rainy day lovers don't hide love inside, they just pass it on.
   Rainy day lovers don't hide love inside, they just pass it on.

Burning Of The Midnight Lamp
Words and music by Jimi Hendrix

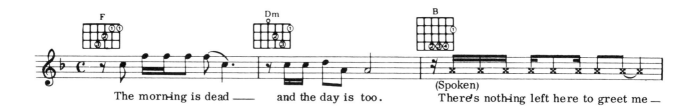

The morn-ing is dead ____ and the day is too.   (Spoken) There's noth-ing left here to greet me ____

but the vel- vet moon. ____ All my lone-li-ness ____ I have felt ____ to- day. ____

It's a lit- tle   more than e-nough   to make a man throw himself a-way, ____ and I con-tin-ue ____

to burn the mid- night lamp ____ a - lone. ____

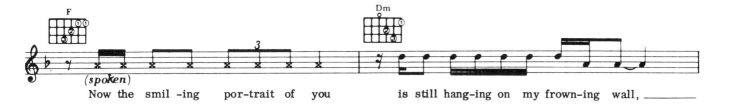

Now the smil-ing por-trait of you is still hang-ing on my frown-ing wall, _____

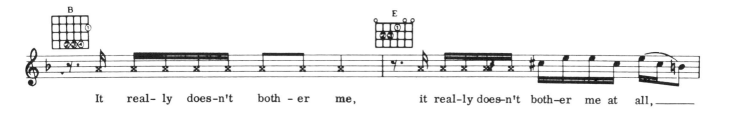

It real-ly does-n't both - er me, it real-ly does-n't both-er me at all, _____

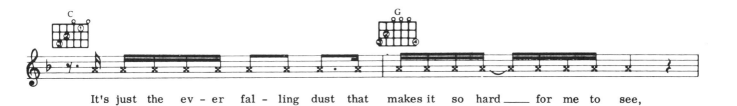

It's just the ev - er fal - ling dust that makes it so hard ____ for me to see,

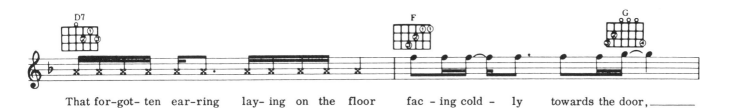

That for-got- ten ear-ring lay- ing on the floor fac - ing cold - ly towards the door, _____

And I con-tin - ue to burn the mid-night lamp _____ all a- lone. _____

His Latest Flame (Marie's The Name)

Words and music by Doc Pomus and Mort Shuman

He was gone but still his words kept re - turnin'.____

What else was there for me to do__ but cry.

Tacet

Would you be - lieve that yes - ter -

day This girl was in my arms and swore to me__

she'd be mine e - ter - nal - ly.__ And Marie's the name

1

of his lat - est flame. A ver-y old

2

flame.____

Honky Tonk Woman

Words and music by Mick Jagger and Keith Richard

Medium Rock

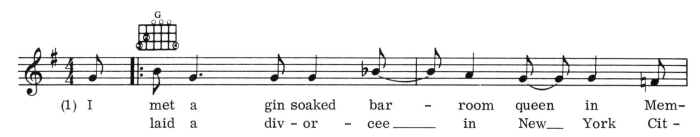

(1) I   met a   gin soaked bar - room queen in Mem-
      laid a   div - or - cee ____ in New__ York Cit -

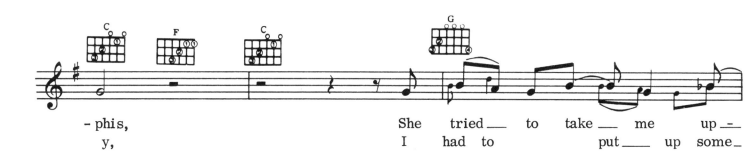

- phis,   She tried __ to take __ me   up __
    y,   I   had to   put __ up some __

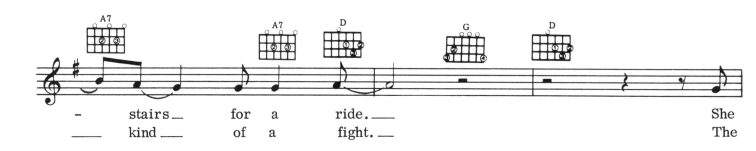

- stairs __ for a   ride. __   She
____ kind __ of a   fight. __   The

had to   heave me right ___ a - cross __ her   should - er,
la - dy   then she cov - ered me __ with   ros - es,

198

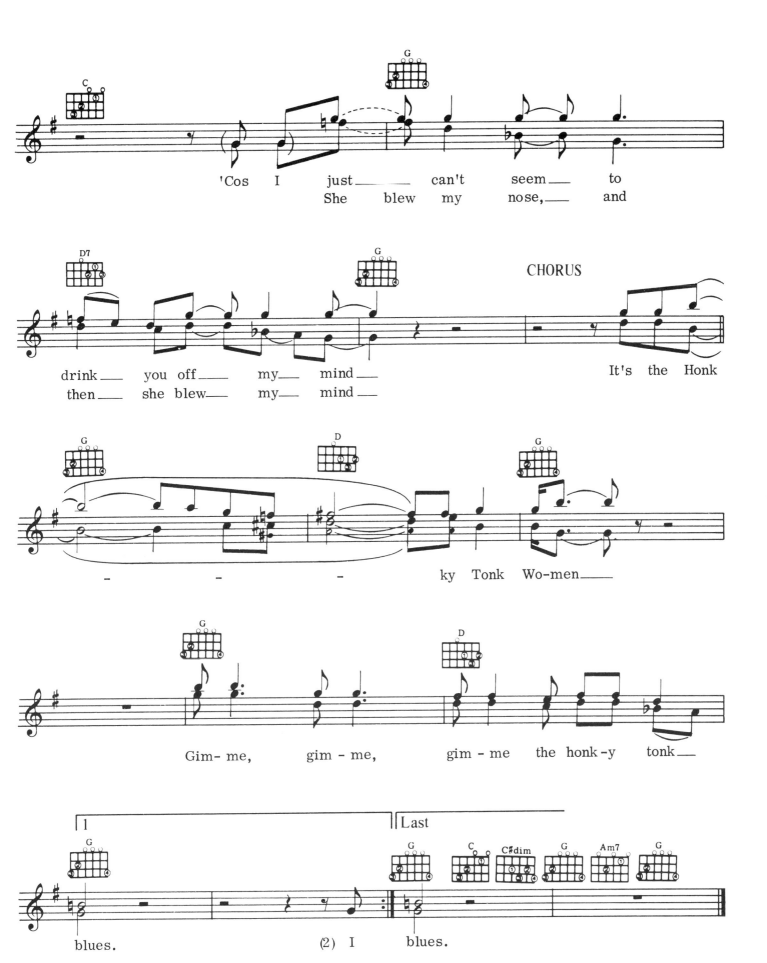

'Cos I just_____ can't seem_____ to
She blew my nose,_____ and

drink____ you off____ my____ mind____
then____ she blew____ my____ mind____

CHORUS

It's the Honk

- - - ky Tonk Wo-men____

Gim- me, gim - me, gim - me the honk-y tonk____

1   Last

blues.   (2) I   blues.

Let It Be

Words and music by John Lennon and Paul McCartney

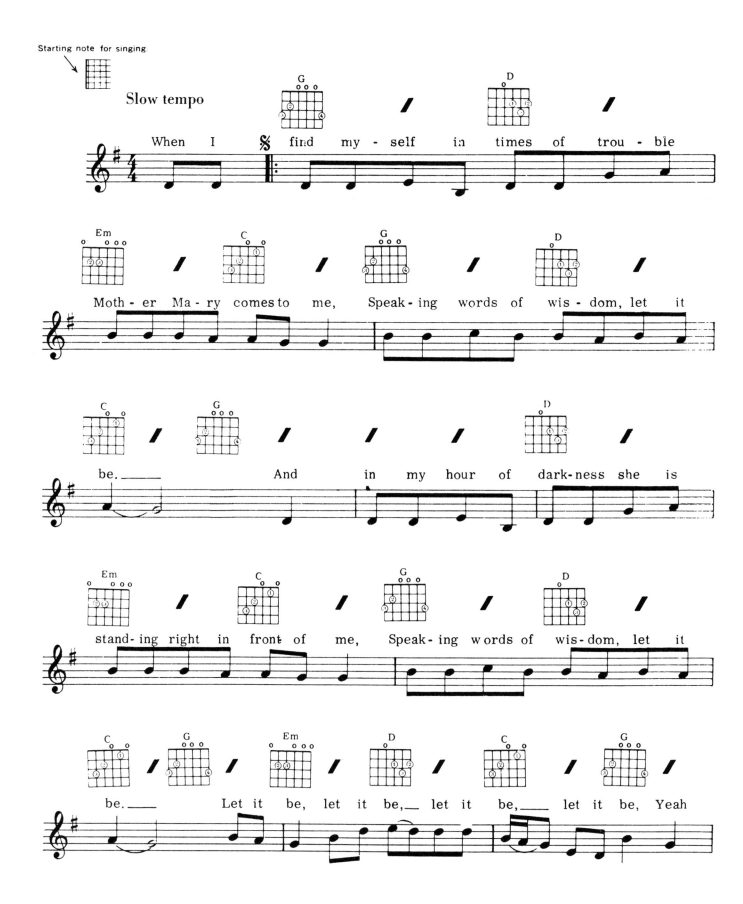

2. And when the broken hearted people
Living in the world agree,
There will be an answer, let it be.
For tho' they may be parted
There is still a chance that they will see,
There will be an answer, let it be.
Let it be, let it be, let it be, let it be,
Yeah There will be an answer, let it be.
Let it be, let it be, let it, be, let it be,
Whisper words of wisdom, let it be.

3. And when the night is cloudy
There is still a light that shines on me,
Shine until tomorrow, let it be.
I wake up to the sound of music
Mother Mary comes to me,
Speaking words of wisdom, let it be.
Let it be, let it be, let it be, let it be,
Yeah There will be an answer, let it be.
Let it be, let it be, let it be, let it be,
Whisper words of wisdom, let it be.

One Of These Nights

Words and music by Glenn Frey and Don Henley

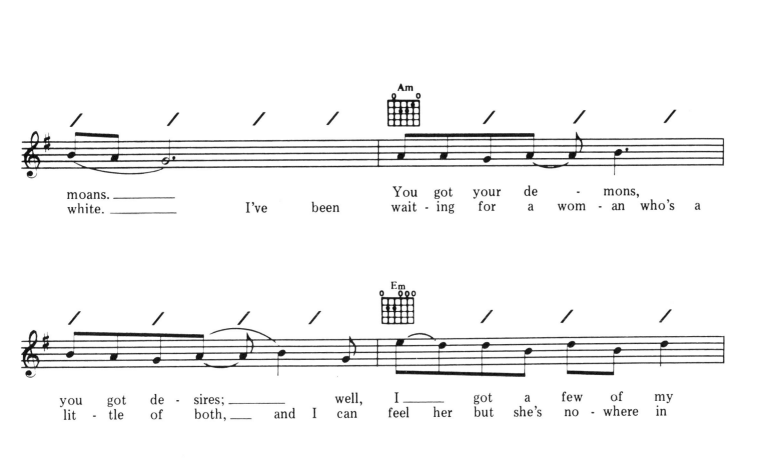

moans. _____   You got your de - mons,
white. _____   I've been   wait - ing for   a wom - an who's a

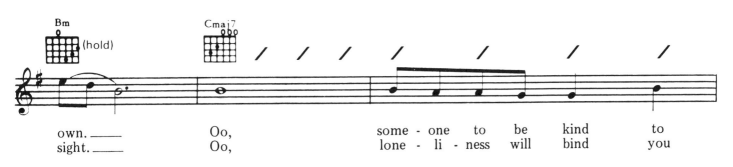

you got de - sires; _____   well, I _____ got   a   few of my
lit - tle of both, ___ and I can   feel her but she's no - where in

own. _____   Oo,   some - one   to   be   kind   to
sight. _____   Oo,   lone - li - ness will bind   you

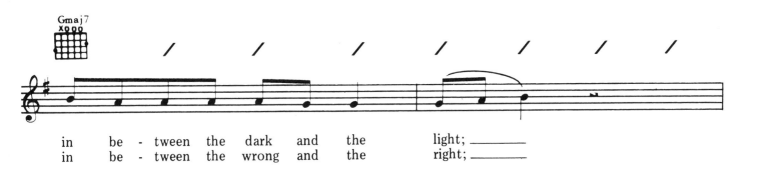

in be - tween the dark   and   the   light; _____
in be - tween the wrong and   the   right; _____

oo,   com - ing right be - hind you, swear I'm gon - na   find   you
oo,   com - ing right be - hind you, swear I'm gon - na   find   you

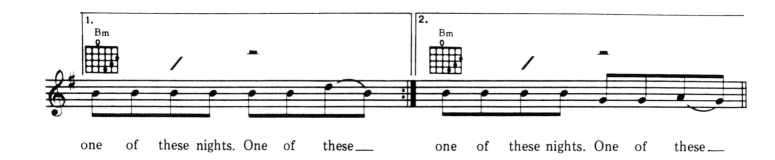

one   of   these nights. One   of   these___   one   of   these nights. One   of   these___

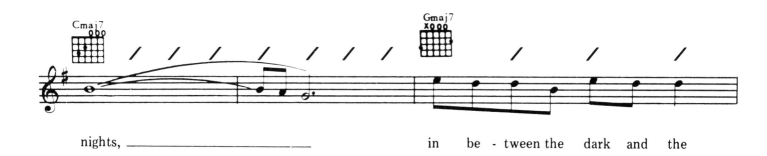

nights, _____   in   be - tween the   dark   and   the

light; ___   com -ing right be - hind   you,   swear I'm gon - na   find   you,

Repeat and fade

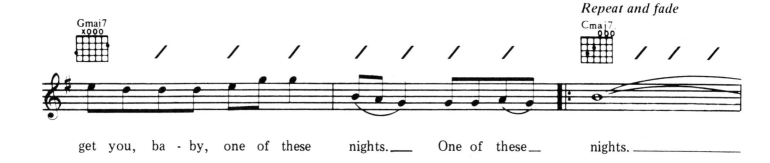

get   you,   ba - by,   one   of these   nights.___   One   of these___   nights. _____

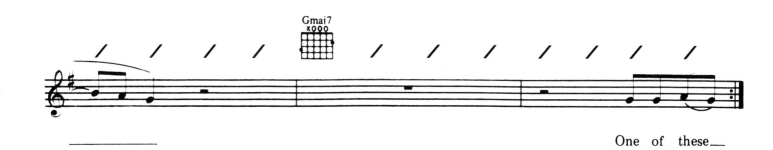

_____   One   of these___

Boulder To Birmingham
Words and music by Bill Danoff and Emmy Lou Harris

grace.   I would walk   all   the   way _____

from Boul - der to Bir - ming - ham __   if I thought I   could

To Coda ⊕

see, _____   I could see __ your   face. ____

D. S. 𝄋 *(no repeats) al Coda* ⊕

Well, you real - ly   got me

Coda
⊕

face. _____   If   I   thought I   could

see, _____   I could see __ your   face. _____

_____

It Never Rains In Southern California

Words and music by Albert Hammond and Mike Hazelwood

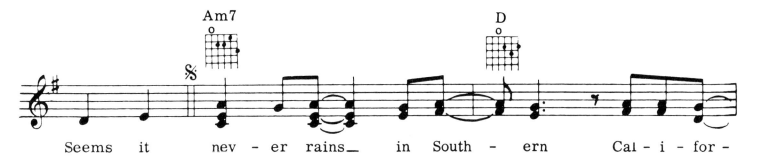

Seems it nev - er rains_ in South - ern Cal - i - for -

- nia,___ Seems I've of - ten heard_ that kind_

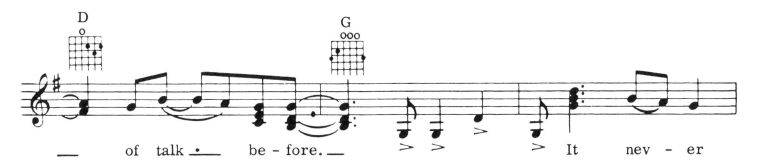

_ of talk be - fore. _ It nev - er

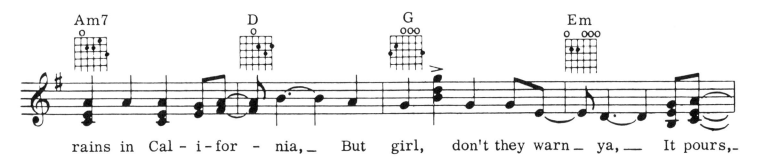

rains in Cal - i - for - nia,_ But girl, don't they warn_ ya, _ It pours,_

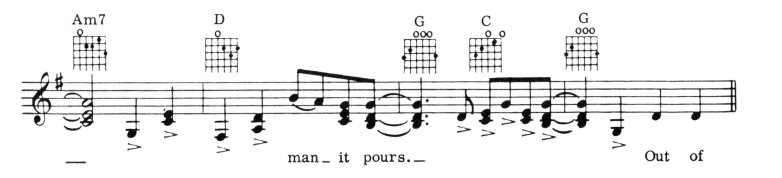

_ man_ it pours._ Out of

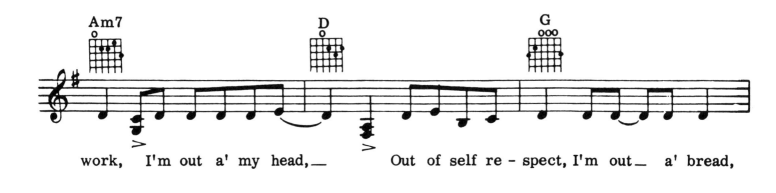

work, I'm out a' my head,__ Out of self re - spect, I'm out__ a' bread,

> I'm un - der - loved, I'm un - der - fed,__ I wan - na go

home. It nev - er rains in Cal - i - for-

- nia,__ But girl, don't they warn__ ya,__ It pours,__

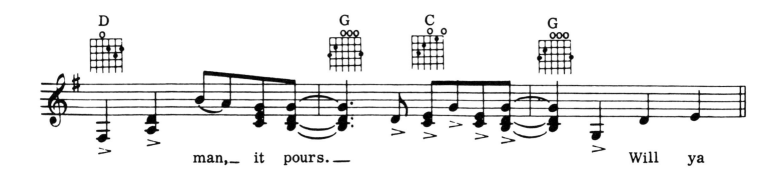

man,__ it pours.__ Will ya

tell   the folks_ back   home _   I near-ly   made it,___

Had of - fers, but_ don't_   know which one___ to take._

_   Please   don't   tell them   how_   you found_

_   me,___   Don't tell them how you found_ me,___ Give me a

break,   Give me a   break.   Seems it

Sunshine Superman

Words and music by Donovan Leitch

Moderato

Sun - shine — came soft - ly thru' my a - win-dow to - day —

— Could have tripped out eas - y, but I've a-changed my ways

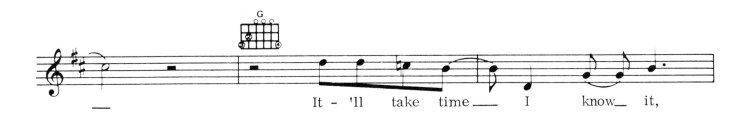

— It - 'll take time — I know — it,

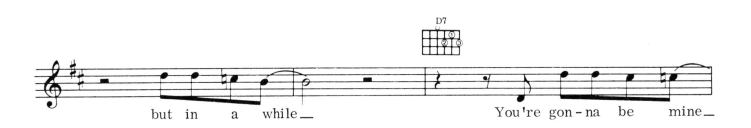

but in a while — You're gon - na be mine —

— and I know it We'll do it in style —

to Coda ⊕

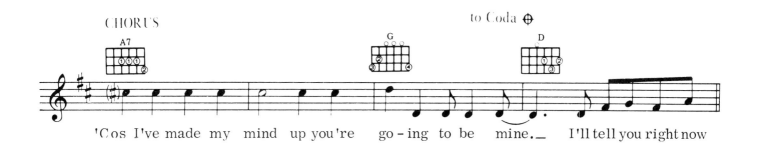

'Cos I've made my mind up you're go-ing to be mine._ I'll tell you right now

an-y trick in the book _ and now ba - by all that I can find_

_ Ev- 'ry - bod-y's hust - ling just to

have a lit-tle scene,_ When I said we'll be cool_

_ I think that you know what I mean,_

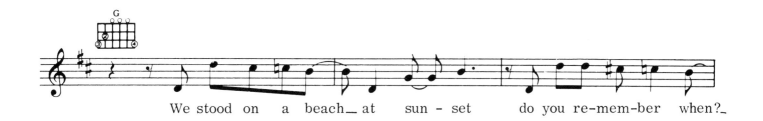

We stood on a beach_ at sun - set do you re-mem-ber when?_

I know a beach___ where day___ fell

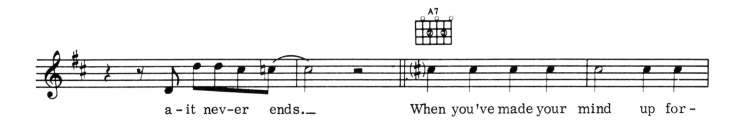

a - it nev-er ends.___ When you've made your mind up for -

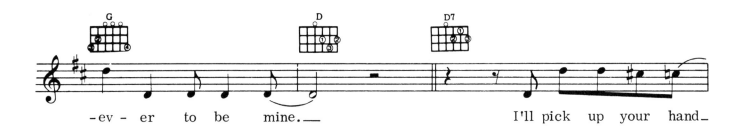

-ev - er to be mine.___ I'll pick up your hand___

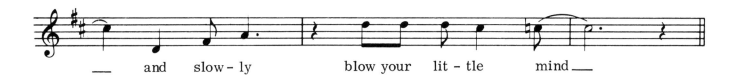

___ and slow - ly blow your lit - tle mind___

D. %. al. Coda

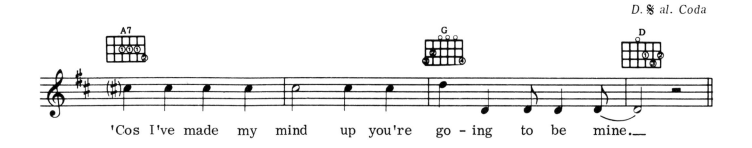

'Cos I've made my mind up you're go - ing to be mine.___

214

CODA

I'll pick up your hand ___ and slow - ly

blow your lit - tle mind ___ When you've made your

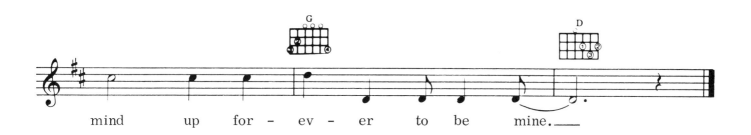

mind up for - ev - er to be mine. ___

Verse (2)   Superman of the lantern ain't got
            A-nothing on me
            I can make like a turtle-in' dove for
            Your problem to see.
            I give you, you can sit there a - thinking
            On your velvet throne
            Down on a rainbow so you can
            A-have all your own.

Chorus (2) When you've made your mind up
            Forever to be mine.

I Can See Clearly Now
Words and music by Johnny Nash

Moderate beat

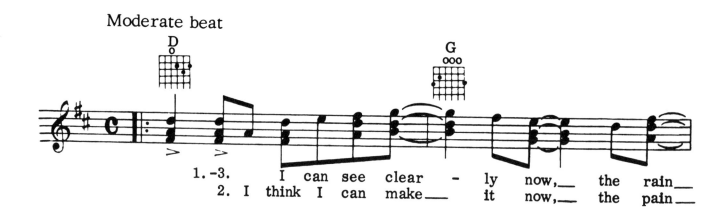

1. -3.   I can see clear - ly now,__ the rain__
2. I think I can make__ it now,__ the pain__

— has gone;__   I can see all_
— has gone;__   All of the bad_

— ob - sta - cles in my way,__
— feel - ings have dis - ap - peared,_

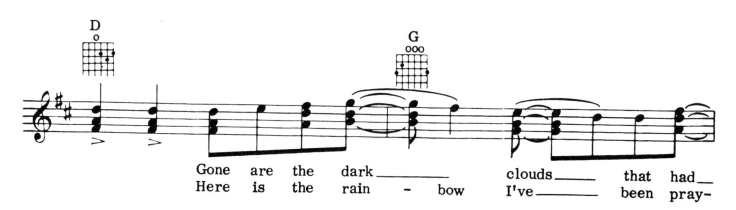

Gone are the dark_____ clouds_____ that had__
Here is the rain - bow I've_____ been pray-

D

_ me blind.__
_ ing for.__

It's gon-na be__ a

C   G   D

To Coda

bright,   bright,__ sun-shin-y day,_____

1.

C   G

It's gon-na be a bright,   bright,__ sun-shin-y day._

2.

D

F

Look all a - round,_____ there's noth - ing but

C   F

blue sky;_____   Look straight a -

217

head,_____ noth - ing but blue sky.

It's gon-na be a bright, bright,_ sun-shin-y day._

Coda

D. C. al Coda

1. D

2. D

218

The First Time Ever I Saw Your Face

Words and music by Ewan MacColl

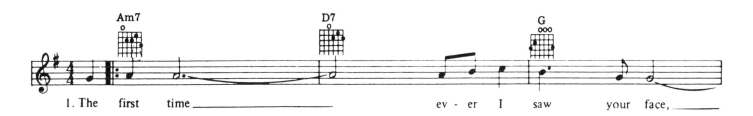

1. The first time _____ ev - er I saw your face, _____

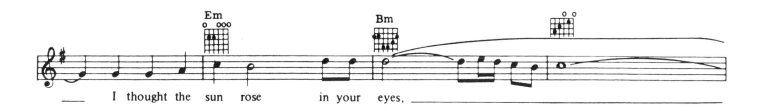

____ I thought the sun rose in your eyes, _____

____ And the moon and stars were the gifts you gave _____ to the

dark _____ and the emp - ty skies, my love, _____

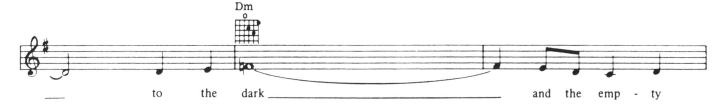

____ to the dark _____ and the emp - ty

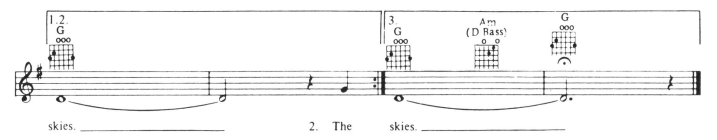

skies. _____   2. The skies. _____

2. The first time ever I kissed your mouth,
   I felt the earth move in my hand,
   Like the trembling heart of a captive bird
   That was there at my command, my love
   That was there at my command.

3. The first time ever I lay with you
   And felt your heart beat close to mine,
   I thought our joy would fill the earth
   And last till the end of time, my love,
   And last till the end of time.

11/96(26164)

New from Music Sales - the one-and only, ultimate busker book! It's *the* book to take to a party... to a gig... on your holiday... or to that famous desert island!

It's packed with literally hundreds and hundreds of the best-loved songs of all time... from vintage standards of the 30s right through to the latest pop hits.

"The Suitcase Book"!

"Probably the best songbook in the world."

The Busker's Fake Book 1001 All-Time Hit Songs

"The only songbook you'll ever need!"

For piano, organ, guitar, all electronic keyboards and all 'C' instruments. With an easy-to-use A-Z title finder plus a classified 'song type' index.

As a taster, here's just a quarter of the titles in this unique bumper songbook...

'A' You're Adorable
A Fine Romance
A Fool Such As I
A Hard Day's Night
A Man And A Woman
A Teenager In Love
Act Naturally
Ain't Misbehavin'
All I Have To Do Is Dream
All My Loving
America
An American In Paris
An Old Fashioned Love Song
Angel Eyes
Another Suitcase In Another Hall
As Time Goes By
Band On The Run
Barbara Ann
Baubles Bangles And Beads
Because
Bennie And The Jets
Big Girls Don't Cry
Big Spender
Bird Dog
Blowin' In The Wind
Boogie Woogie Bugle Boy
Buffalo Gals
Bye Bye Love
California Dreaming
Can't Smile Without You
Candle In The Wind
Caravan
Chantilly Lace
Come Fly With Me
Consider Yourself
Crazy
Cruising Down The River
Dancing Queen
Daniel
Desafinado
Devil In Disguise
Diamonds Are A Girl's Best Friend
Do You Know The Way To San Jose
Don't Cry For Me Argentina
Don't Pay The Ferryman
Don't Sleep In The Subway
EastEnders
Ebony And Ivory
Eleanor Rigby
Every Breath You Take
Empty Chairs At Empty Tables
The Entertainer
First Time Ever I Saw Your Face
Fools Rush In
From Me To You
Funiculi, Funicula
Für Elise
Get Back
Get It On (Bang A Gong)
The Girl From Ipanema
Good Vibrations
Goodbye Yellow Brick Road
Guys And Dolls
Happy Xmas (War Is Over)
Havah Nagilah
He Ain't Heavy He's My Brother
Hello Mary Lou

Hello, Goodbye
Here, There And Everywhere
Hey Jude
Hey, Good Lookin'
Honeysuckle Rose
I Came I Saw I Conga'd
I Don't Want To Spoil The Party
I Dreamed A Dream
I Feel Pretty
I Fought The Law
I Left My Heart In San Francisco
I Saw Her Standing There
I'm A Loser
I'm Beginning To See The Light
I'm Still Standing
If I Had A Hammer
If I Were A Bell
In The Air Tonight
It Never Rains In Southern California
It's Not Unusual
It's So Easy
Jambalaya
Jealous Guy
La Ronde De l'Amour
Lady D'Arbanville
The Lady In Red
The Lambeth Walk
The Last Time I Saw Paris
Layla
Leaning On A Lamp Post
Let It Be
Let's Twist Again
The Lion Sleeps Tonight
Live And Let Die
Long Tall Sally
Love And Marriage
Lover Man
Lucille
Luck Be A Lady
Lullaby Of Birdland
Maple Leaf Rag
Maria
Me And My Girl
Mister Bojangles
Money For Nothing
Mull Of Kintyre
Never On A Sunday
Nights In White Satin
Norwegian Wood
Not Fade Away
O Sole Mio
Oh Pretty Woman
Ol' Man River
Old Shep
On A Slow Boat To China
Only The Lonely
P.S. I Love You
Peggy Sue
Pennies From Heaven
Penny Lane
Pigalle
Poison Ivy
The Power Of Love
Raindrops Keep Falling On My Head
Rave On
Rhapsody In Blue
Riders On The Storm
Rock Around The Clock

Ruby Don't Take Your Love To Town
Satin Doll
Scarborough Fair
Shake Rattle And Roll
She Loves You
Singing The Blues
Sixteen Tons
Sloop John B
Smoke Gets In Your Eyes
Solitude
Something
Somewhere
Spanish Eyes
Standing On The Corner
Stars Fell On Alabama
Stranger In Paradise
Strangers In The Night
Streets Of London
Sugarbush
Sultans Of Swing
Summertime Blues
Sunshine Of Your Love
Sweet Charity
Swing Low, Sweet Chariot
Take Back Your Mink
Take That Look Off Your Face
Take The 'A' Train
Teen Angel
The Tender Trap
That'll Be The Day
Theme For A Dream
These Foolish Things
They Didn't Believe Me
This Guy's In Love With You
This Land Is Your Land
Those Were The Days
Three Little Fishies
Till There Was You
To Know Him Is To Love Him
Tonight
True Love Ways
Tulips From Amsterdam
Tutti Frutti
Unchained Melody
Under The Boardwalk
Up, Up And Away
Uptown Girl
The Very Thought Of You
Wake Up Little Susie
Walk Tall
The Way You Look Tonight
We Can Work It Out
We Don't Need Another Hero
We Shall Overcome
We'll Meet Again
What Kind Of Fool Am I
Wheels
When I'm Sixty Four
When Irish Eyes Are Smiling
When This Lousy War Is Over
Where Have All The Flowers Gone
Witchcraft
With A Little Help From My Friends
Woman
Yellow Submarine
Yesterday
Your Cheatin' Heart
Your Song

Melody, lyrics and guitar chords to literally hundreds and hundreds of the best songs of all time... from the golden standards through to the great pop hits of today.

Wise Publications
Order No. AM 90407

While compiling this huge book, editor/arranger Peter Lavender kept all the artwork in a huge suitcase! But now that it's printed, this new mega-bumper busker book is a lot easier to carry around!

Surprisingly portable, in fact, at the usual songbook size of 12" x 9"... with some 656 pages!

As well as the 1,001 songs, the book includes a handy A-Z alphabetical title index *and* a classified index, too.